चिन्मय ग्रन्थ माला

# GĪTĀ for CHILDREN

(A Teaching Tool for Elders)



Swami Chinmayananda

Central Chinmaya Mission Trust

•

Second Edition 1975 to December 2009 – 64,000 copies
Reprint December 2012 to August 2013 – 2,000 copies
Revised Edition January 2014 – 3,000 copies

•

Published by:
**Chinmaya Prakashan**
The Publications Division of
**Central Chinmaya Mission Trust**
Sandeepany Sadhanalaya
Saki Vihar Road, Mumbai 400072, India
Tel.: +91-22-2857 2367, 2857 5806
Fax: +91-22-2857 3065
Email: ccmtpublications@chinmayamission.com
Website: www.chinmayamission.com

•

Distribution Centre in USA:
**Chinmaya Mission West**
Publications Division
560 Bridgetown Pike, Langhorne, PA 19053, USA
Tel.: 1-888-CMW-READ, (215) 396-0390 Fax: (215) 396-9710
Email: publications@chinmayamission.org
Website: www.chinmayapublications.org

•

Designed by:
Chinmaya Kalpanam, Mumbai

•

Printed by:
SAP Print Solutions Pvt. Ltd., Mumbai

•

Price: ₹ 100/-

•

ISBN 978-81-7597-599-6

CTP

# Contents

## Transliteration and Pronunciation Guide

In the book, Devanāgarī characters are transliterated according to the scheme adopted by the International Congress of Orientalists at Athens in 1912. In it one fixed pronunciation value is given to each letter; f, q, w, x and z are not called to use. An audio recording of this guide is available at http://chinmayamission.com/scriptures.php. According to this scheme:

| Devanāgarī | Translit-eration | Sounds Like | Devanāgarī | Translit-eration | Sounds Like |
|---|---|---|---|---|---|
| अ | a | son | ढ् | ḍh | adhesive* |
| आ | ā | father | ण् | ṇ | under* |
| इ | i | different | त् | t | tabla |
| ई | ī | feel | थ् | th | thumb |
| उ | u | full | द् | d | this |
| ऊ | ū | boot | ध् | dh | Gandhi |
| ऋ | ṛ | rhythm* | न् | n | nose |
| ॠ | ṝ | ** | प् | p | pen |
| ऌ | ḷ | ** | फ् | ph | phantom* |
| ए | e | evade | ब् | b | boil |
| ऐ | ai | delight | भ् | bh | abhor |
| ओ | o | core | म् | m | mind |
| औ | au | now | य् | y | yes |
| क् | k | calm | र् | r | right |
| ख् | kh | khan | ल् | l | love |
| ग् | g | gate | व् | v | very |
| घ् | gh | ghost | श् | ś | shut |
| ङ् | ṅ | ankle* | ष् | ṣ | sugar |
| च् | c | chuckle | स् | s | simple |
| छ् | ch | witch* | ह् | h | happy |
| ज् | j | justice | ं | ṁ | improvise |
| झ् | jh | Jhansi | ः | ḥ | ** |
| ञ् | ñ | banyan | क्ष् | kṣ | action |
| ट् | ṭ | tank | त्र् | tr | three* |
| ठ् | ṭh | ** | ज्ञ् | jñ | gnosis |
| ड् | ḍ | dog | ऽ | ' | a silent 'a' |

* These letters don't have an exact English equivalent. An approximation is given here.

** These sounds cannot be approximated in English words.

We take the opportunity to thank
Mr. Y. Sivasankara Reddy and Mrs. Snehalatha Reddy
for having sponsored the printing of this book
and ensuring that this timeless wisdom
reaches the hands of seekers galore.

# Preface

## To Parents And Mission Workers

The children of today are the citizens of tomorrow. To mould their thoughts and aspirations is the true fulfilment of national education. The ideal given to them in their early childhood alone can again and again inspire them in their future years of life and supply them with the courage to face their problems, the guts to pursue their purposes diligently, faith in themselves and in their country, and the heroism to live and act according to their own convictions. A generation growing up thus, determined to gain their goal, sure of their dignity, consistent in their endeavour and deeply proud of their own cultural past, alone can render a country to grow up to the status of a nation.

In Bhārata, her cultural consciousness is the one chord that binds our different people with different habits, customs, beliefs and faiths together into an integrated, united, self-respecting and fully awakened sense of nationhood. *Śrīmad Bhagavad-gītā* is the quintessence of our entire ancient cultural lore, based upon the irrefutable arguments and inspired thoughts of the ṛṣis, recorded for us in our Upaniṣads.

The Chinmaya Mission Bālavihārs are organising weekly meetings of the children and training them in our ancient culture and our national way of life. We employ various interesting and entertaining techniques to bring these children the flavour and beauty, the light and melody of the Bhāratīya culture – the Hindu philosophy of thoughts and actions.

Now a stage has come when the bālakas and bālikās (boys and girls) growing in this enthralled atmosphere of the Bālavihārs have started demanding to know the meaning and contents of the *Gītā* verses, which they are taught or they have learnt to chant. Mission workers who are in charge of these Bālavihārs themselves find it difficult to explain the deep and profound philosophy of the *Gītā* to the growing children. There are books in the market, written by serious thinkers and students of the *Gītā*, bringing out in their ponderous volumes, the subtle beauty of the sacred thoughts of Lord Kṛṣṇa. But the highly involved arguments expressed in a laborious style, studded with very many quotations from the Upaniṣads and sprinkled with the conclusions of other schools of philosophers, make all such existing volumes useless to the children.

Again, the members of our Bālavihārs are in the age group of 6-12, the juniors; and 12-16, the seniors. The juniors learn to chant the text and they are happy when they can recite from memory chapter after chapter. But when they grow to be in the senior section, they demand explanations and need to know what the *Gītā* says. Here, we found that even our sevakas and sevikās were not able to help the children. Hence, we conceived the idea of bringing out a *Gītā for Children.* These appeared, chapter by chapter in our Mission journal (*Tapovan Prasad*).

Here again, I must admit that the style is not so simple that the children can themselves read and enjoy the thoughts of the 701 verses of the *Gītā*. These chapters were written so that the Chinmaya Mission workers or the intelligent parents of our children may read and digest and then explain these ideas to the members of the Bālavihār classes. Again, we will have to go through this in the vernacular in many of the classes.

This volume, *Gītā for Children* is addressed to the parents and workers of the Bālavihārs. They will read and understand these simple thoughts and thereafter, present these ideas to their wards in the local language, in simple and clear expressions without any hurry or impatience.

Explain these ideas again and again. Make the children discuss them with you.

Let them ask questions.

Let them, among themselves, teach each other what they were taught in the previous classes.

Make thus, the *Gītā*-study lively allowing full participation of the children themselves in all the discussions.

Each chapter recommends a few stanzas which the children must learn by heart and chant them with tune and rhythm. There are some questions suggested at the end of each chapter which are to be discussed. The members must, again and again, be made to answer these questions. When all the members can answer all the questions given therein, then the Mission worker can proceed to the next chapter.

Whenever there is any difficulty for you to understand, please refer to me by a note. I shall try to clarify. You will do well to read my *Gītā* discourses which would supply you with illustrations, stories, examples, and so on which you can use to enliven the children's study hour.

To many parents, this volume would in itself be, I am confident, an education and a helpful initiation into the heart of the *Gītā*.

**CHINMAYANANDA**

Sandeepany Sadhanalaya
Powai-Park Drive, Powai,
Bombay – 400072.
1st October, 1967

# Introduction

## Summary of the *Mahābhārata*

In the old old days, there was an illustrious king, Śantanu by name, ruling at Hastināpura. He had a son, named Bhīṣma more renowned than his father. After Bhīṣma lost his mother, Śantanu married Satyavati, a fisherwoman. Before this marriage, she had already become a mother. Her son was Vyāsa, very famous as a sage and as a writer. It was he who collected and rearranged the Veda chants and compiled them into four volumes. He wrote the purāṇas and the great epic *Mahābhārata*. This great work contains the *Bhagavad-gītā*, the advice of Kṛṣṇa to Arjuna.

The greatness of *Mahābhārata* lies in its quantity and quality. It contains one lakh verses. It is an encyclopedia of all information – social, political, economic, moral, religious, historical, philosophical, legendary, and so on. It is rightly said, 'What is found in *Mahābhārata*, one may find elsewhere in other works but what is not there will not be found in any book at all'. Because it is such a mine of knowledge, and unlike the four Vedas this epic can be read by all, without distinction of training (caste), faith (creed), or ability (gender). It is called the fifth Veda.

Dhṛtarāṣṭra and Pāṇḍu were born to Bhīṣma's brothers. Dhṛtarāṣṭra was born blind and though elder, he had to forfeit his claim to the throne due to this physical defect. Pāṇḍu became king. Of the two brothers Dhṛtarāṣṭra married Gāndhārī, a princess, whereas Pāṇḍu, the younger had two wives, Kuntī and Mādrī. Gāndhārī was so devoted and submissive to her lord that she bandaged her eyes, not to enjoy anything that she could not share with her royal husband and remained thus, voluntarily blind for life. What high ideals! She became the mother of the Kauravas, 100 in number, whereas Kuntī got three sons and Mādrī two. At the death of Pāṇḍu and Mādrī the five Pāṇḍava princes were brought up and educated along with Kaurava boys under the supervision of Bhīṣma and under the patronage of Dhṛtarāṣṭra. Droṇa, though a brāhmin, was a very skilful and efficient teacher who taught them the art of archery and the various techniques of warfare.

Yudhiṣṭhira, the eldest of the Pāṇḍavas was so righteous that he gained the name Dharmaputra. Bhīma, as you have guessed already, was a giant in physical strength. Arjuna was the handsomest and the cleverest of all and most dear to the teacher. Dharmaputra was the beloved of the people and being the eldest among the 105 princes, was naturally and by his right too, the heir to the throne. Duryodhana, the eldest of the Kauravas, however, was jealous of the Pāṇḍavas and tried every means to destroy them. But in our motherland we know that virtue always triumphs. Good conquers evil. 'Satyameva jayate' – Truth alone triumphs.

Duryodhana's plan to kill the Pāṇḍavas cunningly giving poison to Bhīma, burning down the lac-house and so on, failed miserably. Bhīma was strong enough to digest the poison. The Pāṇḍavas were warned in time by their uncle Vidura and so, in the darkness of the night, the five brothers along with their mother escaped into the jungle from the burning lac-house.

After their miraculous escape from the lac-house, they did not return to the palace. They roamed about in the guise of brāhmins with their mother.

Every one including the Kauravas believed them to be dead.

During that time, they heard of the svayaṁvara of Draupadī. The qualification to marry her lay in the extraordinary skill of archery in hitting a moving target. Arjuna easily won. Everybody congratulated the winner and discovered that it was Arjuna. Thus the Pāṇḍavas were found out. He took his bride to their hut and called to his mother to come outside and see what he had brought. Instead of doing so she answered back, "My dear children, whatever it be you share it among yourselves". Therefore Draupadī became the common wife of all the five Pāṇḍavas. Kṛṣṇa, who was also present at the marriage ceremony became a great friend of the Pāṇḍavas from then onwards.

Pāṇḍavas were thus again victorious. On Bhīṣma's advice, the kingdom was divided into two parts. Naturally, the better half was taken away by the Kauravas. Still, the Pāṇḍavas built a wonderful city in their own half and called it Indraprastha.

Duryodhana watching the increasing prosperity of the Pāṇḍavas, could contain himself no longer.

He openly challenged Dharmaputra for a game of dice. Śakunī, deceit in human form, was the uncle of the Kauravas. He played for them. Inevitably Dharmaputra lost everything; his kingdom, his brothers and also his wife.

Not satisfied with this gain, Duryodhana tried to insult Draupadī in public. By Kṛṣṇa's grace nothing disastrous happened. Dhṛtarāṣṭra fearing that this might bring unforeseen calamities begged Draupadī to take whatever she wanted. She asked for the freedom of her husbands. It was granted.

Dhṛtaraṣṭra due to his excessive love for the eldest son was blind to what is right and what is wrong. So again Duryodhana invited Dharmaputra for another game of dice and the bet was that the losers would live in the forest for thirteen years without any claim to the kingdom, the last year however to be spent incognito. But if in the $13^{th}$ year, they were detected, there would be another exile of thirteen years and this would go on for ever.

Dharmaputra again lost. During the twelve years' sojourn in the forests the Pāṇḍavas visited many holy places. They had many interesting adventures at this time. One of them led to Hanumāna's friendship and grace. Arjuna is called Kapidhvaja as he keeps on his flag the emblem of Hanumāna. Kṛṣṇa visited them now and then. Arjuna at the advice of Vyāsa practised penance, propitiated Śiva and got from Him the mighty weapon, the Paśupatāstra. He propitiated also the other gods, Indra, Agni, Varuṇa and others and got from all of them very powerful weapons. Thus the twelve years were not wasted but spent in securing the divine weapons which would become useful later on.

In the 13th year, hiding all their weapons in the hollow of a tree in a burial ground, all the Pāṇḍavas with Draupadī went to the palace of the king of the Virāṭas and stayed there as servants. Duryodhana was making frantic efforts to discover them. When he heard about the strange murder of Kīcaka, the brother-in-law of the king he concluded that the Pāṇḍavas must be in the Virāṭa country. So the Kauravas attacked the Virāṭas, with apparent purpose of carrying away their cattle wealth. Of course, the Pāṇḍavas took part in the battle but when they were recognised as Pāṇḍavas the time limit of thirteen years had already passed.

Dharmaputra was fond of peace and was ever against any quarrel, much less war. So he sent Kṛṣṇa as a messenger to Hastināpura to claim his kingdom back from Duryodhana. But would Duryodhana give? No. He had by this time come to regard Indraprastha as his own. He not only refused to give their kingdom back, but refused to give even five houses for the five brothers to live! Nay, he swore, he would not give even a pinpoint of ground to them.

War had to be declared. This is the great war fought at Kurukṣetra to decide the right of claim. The hundred Kauravas, Bhīṣma, Droṇa, Aśvatthāmā and others were on one side and the Pāṇḍavas, Kṛṣṇa, Drupada, and so on were on the other. Kṛṣṇa did not actually fight. He was the charioteer of Arjuna and hence He is called Pārthasārathy. Kṛṣṇa was very impartial. He gave his army to the Kauravas and himself offered to serve the Pāṇḍavas.

The Kaurava and the Pāṇḍava armies arrayed themselves for the war. The Kauravas planned their attacks under the supervision of Bhīṣma and under Bhīma's management the Pāṇḍava army marched into formation. Arjuna asked Kṛṣṇa to drive his chariot right into the heart of the battlefield into the no-man's land between the two opposing forces so that he could get a clear view of all. He was bubbling over with the war spirit. He faced his enemy forces but there he saw, not his enemies but his revered grandsire Bhīṣma, his beloved teacher Droṇa, and his near and dear kinsmen and friends. He felt a growing weakness in his heart. He lost his enthusiasm to fight. He turned to Kṛṣṇa and told him clearly that he did not wish to fight against his seniors, friends and cousins to win a paltry kingdom. How can he enjoy the luxuries and the glories of a kingdom won by spilling the blood of so many of his relatives and friends!

When he refused to fight, Kṛṣṇa gave him good advice, enlightening him upon where his duty lay. Its essence was active conquest of evil and not passive resistance to it. Arjuna was a different person altogether after he had tasted this spiritual elixir. It cured not only his weakness but revived his spirits. This marvellous advice is the *Bhagavad-gītā* which gives in a nutshell the essence of the vast and deep learning enshrined in the scriptures.

The advice was obviously given by Kṛṣṇa to Arjuna in a battlefield. But it is not in any sense narrow in its scope. It is a universal guide meant for the entire humanity in all times for all times irrespective of age, sex, caste and creed. It was applicable in the age of the purāṇas, that is Dvāpara-yuga in Bhāratavarṣa in the case of Arjuna at the Kurukṣetra war. It is equally applicable in the present Kali-yuga, in any place on the globe, now and forever to every individual young or old, man or woman.

We are a dual personality of good and bad. We must conquer this evil and cultivate the good in us. Starve the demon and feed the God.[1] How? For instance if you are angry and want to smash the nose and break the chin of your friend, you may raise your hand but pause a moment and remember what *Gītā* says, make a rapid review of the *Gītā* and then proceed. You shall find it easier and wiser to smash his entire being more effectively and with less effort and procure him as a slave till death by shaking hands

---

[1] एतैर्विमुक्तः कौन्तेय तमोद्वारैस्त्रिभिर्नरः ।
आचरत्यात्मनः श्रेयस्ततो याति परां गतिम् ॥ १६·२२ ॥
*etairvimuktaḥ kaunteya tamodvāraistribhirnaraḥ,*
*ācaratyātmanaḥ śreyastato yāti parāṁ gatim.* (16.22)

16.22. A man who is liberated from these three gates to darkness, O Kaunteya, practises what is good for him and thus goes to the supreme goal.

with him. Patience, forgiveness, friendship[1] that is what *Gītā* teaches us. So do not do anything rashly and in haste. Then you may come to suffer and regret. Always see first whether *Gītā* offers any solution. Follow the instructions of the *Gītā*. The duty of Arjuna, a Kṣatriya prince is to conquer his enemies[2]. The duty of students is to study, acquire pure faultless learning. The duty of a cobbler is to mend shoes well and of a butcher to supply meat to the needy. Well, *Gītā* teaches us to discharge our duties and to put our

---

[1] अहिंसा सत्यमक्रोधस्त्यागः शान्तिरपैशुनम् ।
दया भूतेष्वलोलुप्त्वं मार्दवं ह्रीरचापलम् ॥ १६·२ ॥
तेजः क्षमा धृतिः शौचमद्रोहो नातिमानिता ।
भवन्ति सम्पदं दैवीमभिजातस्य भारत ॥ १६·३ ॥
*ahiṁsā satyamakrodhastyāgaḥ śāntirapaiśunam,*
*dayā bhūteṣvaloluptvaṁ mārdavaṁ hrīracāpalam.* (16.2)
*tejaḥ kṣamā dhṛtiḥ śaucamadroho nātimānitā,*
*bhavanti sampadaṁ daivīmabhijātasya bhārata.* (16.3)

16.2. Harmlessness, truth, absence of anger, renunciation, peacefulness, absence of crookedness, compassion to beings, uncovetousness, gentleness, modesty, absence of fickleness.

16.3. Vigour, forgiveness, fortitude, purity, absence of hatred, absence of pride – these belong to the one born for the divine Estate, O Bhārata.

[2] स्वधर्ममपि चावेक्ष्य न विकम्पितुमर्हसि ।
धर्म्याद्धि युद्धाच्छ्रेयोऽन्यत्क्षत्रियस्य न विद्यते ॥ २·३१ ॥
*svadharmamapi cāvekṣya na vikampitumarhasi,*
*dharmyāddhi yuddhācchreyo'nyatkṣatriyasya na vidyate.* (2.31)

2.31. Further, looking at thine own duty thou ought not to waver, for there is nothing higher for a kṣatriya than a righteous war.

whole heart into them, regardless of the outcome[1]. Evidently, then there would be no such word as 'failure' in our life.

---

[1] शौर्यं तेजो धृतिर्दाक्ष्यं युद्धे चाप्यपलायनम् ।
दानमीश्वरभावश्च क्षात्रं कर्म स्वभावजम् ॥ १८·४३ ॥

*śauryaṁ tejo dhṛtirdākṣyaṁ yuddhe cāpyapalāyanam,*
*dānamīśvarabhāvaśca kṣātraṁ karma svabhāvajam.* (18.43)

18.43. Prowess, splendour, firmness, dexterity and also not fleeing from battle, generosity, lordliness – these are the duties of the kṣatriyas, born of (their) own nature.

सहजं कर्म कौन्तेय सदोषमपि न त्यजेत् ।
सर्वारम्भा हि दोषेण धूमेनाग्निरिवावृताः ॥ १८·४८ ॥

*sahajaṁ karma kaunteya sadoṣamapi na tyajet,*
*sarvārambhā hi doṣeṇa dhūmenāgnirivāvṛtāḥ.* (18.48)

18.48. One should not abandon, O Kaunteya, the duty to which one is born, though faulty; for all undertakings are enveloped by evil as fire by smoke.

हतो वा प्राप्स्यसि स्वर्गं जित्वा वा भोक्ष्यसे महीम् ।
तस्मादुत्तिष्ठ कौन्तेय युद्धाय कृतनिश्चयः ॥ २·३७ ॥

*hato vā prāpsyasi svargaṁ jitvā vā bhokṣyase mahīm,*
*tasmāduttiṣṭha kaunteya yuddhāya kṛtaniścayaḥ.* (2.37)

2.37. Slain thou will obtain heaven; victorious you will enjoy the earth; therefore, stand up, O son of Kuntī, resolve to fight.

नियतं सङ्गरहितमरागद्वेषतः कृतम् ।
अफलप्रेप्सुना कर्म यत्तत्सात्त्विकमुच्यते ॥ १८·२३ ॥

*niyataṁ saṅgarahitamarāgadveṣataḥ kṛtam,*
*aphalaprepsunā karma yattatsāttvikamucyate.* (18.23)

18.23. An action which is ordained, which is free from attachment, which is done without love or hatred, by one, not desirous of the fruit, that action is declared to be sāttvika (pure).

*Bhagavad-gītā* is a practical guide. It teaches the art of living this life in harmony with the spiritual one. It teaches the art of self-discipline and self-perfection. Man is a synthesis of matter and spirit and nobody can afford to ignore the one in order to perfect the other. We have to blend them in proper proportions, assigning their due importance to both. *Gītā* is really a treasure-house of one of the most precious pearls of wisdom. It offers a solution to all our personal problems, though they vary in nature from individual to individual. There lies the simple beauty of the *Bhagavad-gītā*.

The Lord's song divine is in the form of a dialogue between two characters Arjuna and Kṛṣṇa – Nara and Nārāyaṇa – wherein Nara symbolises man and Nārāyaṇa represents the refuge of man, God. The God directs and guides the dejected, depressed, helpless and erring man along the right path. This struggle in man between himself and the Lord of his heart and ultimately the Lord coming to his rescue when he surrenders to Him are quite common in our everyday life. But generally we fail to notice the play of God in our day-to-day activities.

*Gītā* is a poem in eighteen chapters[1], containing 701 stanzas. The philosophy preached in these lyrical stanzas constitutes the Bhārata culture, the time honoured culture of our forefathers, the very glory of our nation. We shall now try to understand what Lord Kṛṣṇa declared about us in each chapter.

[1] Kurukṣetra war was fought for 18 days. 18 divisions of soldiers (akṣauhiṇis) took part in it ,11 on the side of the kauravas and 7 on the side of the Pāṇḍavas. One akṣauhiṇi contains soldiers in chariot, on horseback, on elephants and on foot and the number in each is a multiple of 18. Besides this, *Mahābhārata* itself contains 18 books (parvas). The purāṇas also are 18 in number. Thus, the number 18 seems to be a favourite number of our ancients.

# Chapter I

## Arjuna – viṣāda – yoga

(Yoga of Arjuna's Grief)

[The dejection of Arjuna – Arjuna feels sad at the prospect of fighting against his kith and kin. When you feel that an injustice has been done against you, and you know the tyrant and want to hit back, but you realise you have not the strength to avenge, the consequent feeling of helpless impotency under which you come to lose your balance is called 'dejection'.]

In the Kurukṣetra battlefield, the armies of the Pāṇḍavas and the Kauravas faced each other. Duryodhana approached Droṇa and said to him, "Revered teacher, see the vast army of the Pāṇḍavas arranged by your student Dhṛṣṭadyumna, the son of Drupada. There, do you not see the great heroes Bhīma, Arjuna, Sātyaki, Virāṭa, Drupada, Dhṛṣṭaketu, Cekitāna, king of Kāśī, Purujit Kuntibhoja, Śaibya, Yudhāmanyu, Uttamaujās, Abhimanyu and the five sons of Draupadī? Look at the valiant leaders of our army also. You yourself, Bhīṣma, Karṇa,

Kṛpa, Aśvatthāmā, Vikarṇa, Bhūriśravā and many others equally great and ready to give up their lives for me. Our army, commanded by Bhīṣma is yet definitely efficient (aparyāptam) compared to that of the Pāṇḍavas under the command of Bhīma[1]. Now, all of us, each leading his division of the army, should strengthen the hands of Bhīṣma, our general".

At this time Bhīṣma blew his conch loudly. This was taken as the first war cry and the others followed it up with their drums, trumpets and conches. The resulting noice was, of course, terrific and deafened the quarters. The challenge of the Kauravas was answered suitably by Arjuna, Kṛṣṇa and others, blowing their own conches. Thus the war cries rose up, echoed and re-echoed throughout the entire area. Both the parties announced thus that they were ready to fight.

Arjuna, full of martial valour and impatient to discharge the first arrow, addressed Kṛṣṇa: "Kṛṣṇa,

---

[1] अपर्याप्तं तदस्माकं बलं भीष्माभिरक्षितम् ।
पर्याप्तं त्विदमेतेषां बलं भीमाभिरक्षितम् ॥ १-१० ॥
*aparyāptaṁ tadasmākaṁ balaṁ bhīṣmābhirakṣitam,*
*paryāptaṁ tvidameteṣāṁ balaṁ bhīmābhirakṣitam.* (1.10)

1.10. This army of ours defended by Bhīṣma is unlimited, whereas that army of theirs defended by Bhīma is limited.

drive on my chariot and stop it in between the two armies, so that I can have a clear view of my opponents, arrayed in support of the wicked Duryodhana".

Kṛṣṇa obeyed his behest. Arjuna cast his eyes over the entire battlefield. Strangely, he saw there not his enemies but his dear uncles, grand-uncles, revered teachers, beloved brothers, friends and cousins. Suddenly he saw, as it were, in a flash, the sad outcome of the war. He felt weak all over.

Softly and gently, the Pāṇḍava prince addressed Lord Kṛṣṇa: "O Kṛṣṇa, seeing these near and dear ones organised so eagerly to fight, my body feels weak all over; my mouth is dry; I tremble. My Gāṇḍīva bow is slipping from my hand. My skin is burning, as it were. I cannot even stand. My mind wanders. Friend, I see only bad omens on all sides. What good will it do me, if I kill my kinsmen in the war? Honestly, I do not court victory. I do not want the kingdom, much less its pleasure. What happiness can I discover in the possession of kingdom, or in the royal pleasures, nay, in my very existence, when these dear ones facing me now are all dead or tragically wounded? I do not wish to kill them, though they wish to kill me; no, not even if I gain the entire three worlds; how much less I care to fight for this tiny worthless kingdom!

What ultimate happiness can we gain by killing our cousins, the Kauravas? Certainly, we gain only sin. So, it is not proper for us to kill the Kauravas.

Killing one's relatives cannot give one, in the end, any happiness. Because they are greedy, they may not see anything bad in killing their relatives and friends. Why cannot we, who see so clearly the tragedy of it all, turn away from this horrible war? O Kṛṣṇa, can you not understand that war brings a chain of sorrows and disasters? War kills and destroys and families are broken. When families are ruined, religious rites automatically cease. The result is impiety. Consequently the women go astray and the rhythm of action in society (varṇas) disappears. The indiscriminate mixing of 'types' hurls those who are responsible for it, into hell. Not only themselves, the very dead forefathers of these sinners too come to suffer! These sinners only are responsible for the downfall and ruin of the social web and the family integrity. It is said that such sinners go to hell and reside there till eternity. Do you not know Kṛṣṇa that now we are going to commit a great crime, prompted by our own greed for a mere piece of earth and its pleasures? Yes, it would be better for me if I am killed, unresisted and unopposed, by these Kauravas".

Saying thus, Arjuna, feeling extremely sad, threw down his bow and arrows and sank on to the seat in the chariot. The Pāṇḍava prince was in utter dejection. He got into a hysterical condition of inner confusions.

It is to such a Pārtha that Lord Kṛṣṇa advises the entire *Gītā*. The *Gītā* gives us a plan and a technique by which we too can successfully come out of our own Arjuna-mood whenever we are in it. The Lord's song contains a secret cure for this dejection in life, which we may call as 'the Kṛṣṇa-specific for the Arjuna disease'.

---

धृतराष्ट्र उवाच
धर्मक्षेत्रे कुरुक्षेत्रे समवेता युयुत्सवः ।
मामकाः पाण्डवाश्चैव किमकुर्वत सञ्जय ॥१·१॥

*dhṛtarāṣṭra uvāca*
*dharmakṣetre kurukṣetre samavetā yuyutsavaḥ,*
*māmakāḥ pāṇḍavāścaiva kimakurvata sañjaya.* (1.1)

1.1. Dhṛtarāṣṭra said: What did the sons of Pāṇḍu and also my people do when they assembled together on the holy plain of Kurukṣetra, desirous to fight, O Sañjaya?

सञ्जय उवाच
अपर्याप्तं तदस्माकं बलं भीष्माभिरक्षितम् ।
पर्याप्तं त्विदमेतेषां बलं भीमाभिरक्षितम् ॥ १·१० ॥

*sañjaya uvāca*

*aparyāptaṁ tadasmākaṁ balaṁ bhīṣmābhirakṣitam,*
*paryāptaṁ tvidameteṣāṁ balaṁ bhīmābhirakṣitam.* (1.10)

1.10. Sañjaya said: This army of ours (said Duryodhana) defended by Bhīṣma is unlimited, whereas that army of theirs defended by Bhīma is limited. (Or) This army of ours protected by Bhīṣma is unlimited, whereas that army of theirs protected by Bhīma is limited.

ततः श्वेतैर्हयैर्युक्ते महति स्यन्दने स्थितौ ।
माधवः पाण्डवश्चैव दिव्यौ शङ्खौ प्रदध्मतुः ॥ १·१४ ॥

*tataḥ śvetairhayairyukte mahati syandane sthitau,*
*mādhavaḥ pāṇḍavaścaiva divyau śaṅkhau*
*pradadhmatuḥ.* (1.14)

1.14. Then, also, Mādhava and the son of Pāṇḍu, seated in their magnificent chariot, yoked with white horses, blew their divine conches.

अर्जुन उवाच
सेनयोरुभयोर्मध्ये रथं स्थापय मेऽच्युत ॥१·२१ ॥

*arjuna uvāca*

*senayorubhayormadhye rathaṁ sthāpaya me'cyuta.* (1.21)

यावदेतान्निरीक्षेऽहं योद्धुकामानवस्थितान् ॥१·२२॥

*yāvadetānnirīkṣe'haṁ yoddhukāmānavasthitān.* (1.22)

1.21 and 1.22. Arjuna said: In the midst of the two armies, place my chariot, O Acyuta, so that I may behold those who stand here desirous to fight.

दृष्ट्वेमं स्वजनं कृष्ण युयुत्सुं समुपस्थितम् ॥१·२८॥

*dṛṣṭvemaṁ svajanaṁ kṛṣṇa yuyutsuṁ*
*samupasthitam.* (1.28)

सीदन्ति मम गात्राणि मुखं च परिशुष्यति।
वेपथुश्च शरीरे मे रोमहर्षश्च जायते ॥१·२९॥

*sīdanti mama gātrāṇi mukhaṁ ca pariśuṣyati,*
*vepathuśca śarīre me romaharṣaśca jāyate.* (1.29)

1.28 and 1.29. Seeing these my kinsmen, O Kṛṣṇa, arrayed, eager to fight, my limbs fail and my mouth is parched. My body quivers and my hair stands on end.

गाण्डीवं स्त्रंसते हस्तात्त्वक्चैव परिदह्यते ॥ १-३० ॥

*gāṇḍīvaṁ, sraṁsate hastāttvakcaiva paridahyate.* (1.30)

1.30. The gāṅḍīva-bow slips from my hand, and my skin burns all over.

निहत्य धार्तराष्ट्रान्नः का प्रीतिः स्याज्जनार्दन ।
पापमेवाश्रयेदस्मान्हत्वैतानाततायिनः ॥ १-३६ ॥

*nihatya dhārtarāṣṭrānnaḥ kā prītiḥ syājjanārdana,*
*pāpamevāśrayedasmānhatvaitānātatāyinaḥ.* (1.36)

1.36. Killing these sons of Dhṛtarāṣṭra what pleasure can be ours, O Janārdana? Sin alone will be our gain by killing these felons.

---

## Questions on Chapter 1

1 What was the question Dhṛtarāṣṭra put to Sañjaya? (1),

2 How did Sañjaya paint the picture of the battlefield in 'Kurukṣetra'? (2)

3 What was the psychological condition of Duryodhana in the battlefield? (3-11)

4 What did Bhīṣma do in order to cheer up Duryodhana and what happened? (12)

5 What did Arjuna say to Lord Kṛṣṇa after hearing the tumultuous sound of conches? (20-23)

6 What was the mental condition of Arjuna who was seated in the chariot, which was placed in the midst of the two armies? (24-27)

7 Give in his own words an account of Arjuna's despondency. (28-33)

8 What are the arguments Arjuna gave in favour of his action? (34-39)

9 Explain in a few sentences, the culture of that period in which Arjuna lived, collecting your data from Arjuna's own arguments in this chapter.

# Chapter II

## Sāṅkhya-yoga

(Yoga of Knowledge – Sāṅkhya)

[Kṛṣṇa, so far a silent listener, now spoke to Arjuna to cheer him up and to revive his spirits. This chapter is said to contain all the essential teachings of the whole *Gītā*, perishable body, imperishable soul, importance of discharging one's duty, selfless action and the Man of Perfect Wisdom.]

Lord Kṛṣṇa: "Arjuna, are you not ashamed to behave in this disgraceful way at this critical moment, now in the face of a war? Do not become a slave to such weakness. It does not befit you, O Prince! Shake off this silly weakness. Stand up and fight".

Arjuna : "How can you ask me to discharge deadly arrows at Bhīṣma and Droṇa, who deserve only devotion and reverence from me? It is better for me to live on alms than to kill these elders and thereby come to enjoy the pleasures, all stained with their blood. I do not also know which is better, to win or to lose. For, we would not wish even to live, after killing the Kauravas. I am overwhelmed with pity. I cannot distinguish the right from the wrong. But I am sure on this point, an unrivalled kingdom, nay even the lordship over the gods will not remove my present mental grief. Tell me, Kṛṣṇa, what is good for me. You are my only refuge. I am Thy disciple. Teach me".

[The Lord, smiling, explains to him the imperishable nature of the soul and the perishable nature of the body and thus shows him the correct path of duty.]

Lord Kṛṣṇa: "You are unnecessarily wasting your grief upon a fact which deserves it the least. At the same time, you seem to speak like a wise person. The really wise do neither grieve for the 'departed' nor for the 'not yet departed', (that is, the living). For, you, I and these kings were never non-existent. Such a time also will not come when we cease to exist. The body will die one day but we still remain forever".

Arjuna : "How can you say so, Kṛṣṇa, when we see death all around us?"

Lord Kṛṣṇa: "In this very body do we not experience childhood, youth and old age? The death of childhood is the birth of youth; the death of youth is the birth of old age. Do these changes affect you? So too, is death. Rebirth is only a change of residence for the soul. There is no pain; and there is a perfect continuity.

The wise understand this and hence, do not grieve over the inevitable. The contact of the sense organs with the objects gives rise to heat and cold, joy and sorrow. Nobody can escape them. They are momentary. Endure them bravely. The wise are not affected in the least by them, and qualify themselves for immortality.

[The imperishable nature of the soul is then set forth in detail.]

The non-existent can never really exist. The eternally Existent can never cease to be. The wise know this eternal Truth".

Arjuna: "What is it, that is real and always existent?"

Lord Kṛṣṇa: "Know that the all-pervading Self is eternally existent. Nobody can destroy it. But the body through which this eternal, indestructible Spirit expresses is perishable. So why do you not fight? One who thinks that the Spirit kills or that the Spirit is killed is a fool. The Spirit does not kill, nor can it ever be killed. It knows neither birth nor death. It cannot come to exist or cease to exist. It is unborn, eternal, changeless and ancient. It is not slain when the body is slain. When one knows the Self to be indestructible, eternal and changeless, tell me, Arjuna, who kills whom?

Just as we discard old clothes and put on new ones, the 'embodied' casts off its useless body taking on new one. Weapons do not injure the Self. Fire does not burn it. Water does not drench it. Wind does not dry it. Thus, the Self cannot be affected by anything. It, at all times, remains as ever lasting, all-pervading, stable, immovable and ancient. It cannot be perceived by the naked eye. It cannot be defined in words. It cannot be changed by time. When you know the nature of the soul, where is the scope for grief?

Even if you do not accept the presence of the eternal Self and consider that each individual undergoes birth and death, why should you give way to grief? For the one that undergoes birth, experience of death also must come. Change is inevitable".

Arjuna: "We do not know what happens before birth and after death. We know only something about this life that stretches between the birth and the death".

Lord Kṛṣṇa: "Even if this be your knowledge of life, still why should you hesitate to act?

Many have pondered deeply over the nature of the Spirit. Some see It as a marvel, others describe It so; still others hear It as a marvel. But the greatest surprise, the marvel of all marvels, is that none really understands It, even though explained.

The Spirit is always indestructible, and hence, it is futile to grieve at the death of the perishable creatures".

> [The necessity for discharging one's duty: the unavoidable compulsion in life that one must do one's duties.]

Arjuna: "If birth and death are inevitable, then what should I do with this life, Kṛṣṇa?"

Lord Kṛṣṇa: "Arjuna! As a kṣatriya,[1] it is your duty by birth to fight every righteous war. Only to the fortunate among the kṣatriyas comes such a war, opening, as it were, the very gates of heaven. So if you do not take part in this righteous war, not only will you fail in discharging your duty to the society, but you will also be foolishly rejecting all fame in life and perpetrating unconsciously a meaningless crime. That disgrace will last for ever. What worse lot than disgrace and dishonour can befall you, who has been always honoured as the greatest hero! Dishonour is indeed more tragic than death for a hero! Whatever your reasons be, the great warriors will conclude that you have run away from the battlefield out of fear. Those who have honoured you in the past will hold you in contempt hereafter, and speak ill of you. Can there be anything more painful than this? Arjuna, my friend, just think of this. If you are killed, you gain heaven; if you win you gain the kingdom. Therefore, get up, determined to fight. Look at joy and sorrow,

---

[1] शौर्यं तेजो धृतिर्दाक्ष्यं युद्धे चाप्यपलायनम् ।
दानमीश्वरभावश्च क्षात्रं कर्म स्वभावजम् ॥ १८·४३ ॥

*śauryaṁ tejo dhṛtirdākṣyaṁ yuddhe cāpyapalāyanam,*
*dānamīśvarabhāvaśca kṣātraṁ karma svabhāvajam.* (18.43)

18.43. Prowess, splendour, firmness, dexterity and also not fleeing from battle, generosity, lordliness – these are the duties of the kṣatriyas, born of (their) own nature.

gain and loss, victory and defeat with the same attitude. With such determination and faith, fight; you shall not thereby, commit any sin.

> [Kṛṣṇa after expounding the eternal nature of the soul and the importance of discharging one's duty, teaches Arjuna the art of Self-perfection attained through selfless, dedicated work in serving society. Mānava-sevā with devotion and humility is Mādhava-pūjā.]

So far, I was explaining to you the philosophy of wisdom (jñāna-yoga). I shall now teach you the philosophy of 'action' (karma-yoga) – how in a spirit of dedication, you can wholeheartedly plunge into action with a mind free from all anxieties for enjoying the fruits that might come out of them. You shall not then be tied down to the bondage caused by action. Such dedicated actions, unlike sacrificial rites, are not wasted, even if left incomplete, nor do they bring harm. Moreover, such dedicated action, even if it be simple and insignificant, saves us from the fear and sufferings of mental agitations. One performs such actions with single-minded devotion and, therefore, one succeeds easily and enjoys peace and joy, whereas the mind usually gets confused and distracted in the process of action by endless thoughts and anxieties for its results. Such anxiety will only lead to failure in this world.

You should not be led away by the meaningless arguments of the Vaidika scholars, who give undue importance to sacrifices, promising heaven as the highest and the most covetable reward. The elaborate sacrificial rites may take one to heaven, but you see, the joys of heaven are finite. How can the mind of one clinging to temporary joys and power be firm and resolute? How can they concentrate on and understand the Highest, the Supreme?

Besides, the scope of Vedas is limited to the three 'temperaments' (guṇas): sattva, rajas and tamas. You must transcend these. Be ever pure and free from the effects of the pairs of 'opposites' – joy and sorrow, health and disease, success and failure, honour and disgrace, praise and censure – the relative experiences. You must also be free from the thought of acquisition and aggrandisement. Be always established in the Supreme. To one, who knows this Brahman, the Supreme, the Vedas and the prescribed rites are only as useful as a small well, when there is a flood up to the roof level. The knowledge of Brahman leads to infinite joy, whereas the performance of sacrifices secures only finite joys.

> [Dedicated action is the path to knowledge. Through selfless service to the world we can grow within to experience the supreme Lord, dwelling in our own hearts.]

Our duty is only to work, to act. Never to worry and have anxieties regarding all the possible results. Do not work with a motive to gain something. At the same time, remember, you do not turn away from your duty and remain idle. With single-minded determination, do your duty, regardless of success and failure. One who acts for the sake of action is the happiest. Others, who act for results are most miserable.

If you really understand this truth, there is no bondage produced by good as well as by bad actions. So, strive for this yoga, which in other words, is efficiency in action. When you shake off your obsession for the results of your actions, you are really a wise and enlightened soul. There will be no confusion in your mind, even when you hear meaningless arguments. You will attain yoga when you are thus, firm and resolute in your stand.

[Here, Arjuna interrupts and asks Kṛṣṇa to define the Man of Steady Wisdom (sthitaprajña), to explain what is perfect wisdom, and to describe the characteristics of such a great saint.]

One who is always content, abandoning all desires and cravings for worldly objects is a Man of Perfect Wisdom. He is not sad in sorrows. He does not rejoice in joys. He is free from attachments, fear and anger. His mind is completely unattached to anything. He is the same in prosperity and adversity. You can attain this steadiness of mind only when you can readily withdraw your sense organs from their objects, just as the tortoise does with its limbs. It is not enough if one forcibly turns away his ears and eyes or mind not to covet the perishable earthly objects. He is the pure one, in whom such cravings are totally dead.

But Arjuna, do not think one can cultivate and develop this attitude easily. The senses are very powerful. They pull the mind in the opposite direction. So, one must try hard to bring one's senses well under control and fix one's mind on Me. One who can thus conquer his unruly senses is a Man of Perfect Wisdom".

[The process of controlling the senses has the various techniques by which our senses can be tamed and brought under perfect control.]

Arjuna: "The process which you explained to me to bring the senses under control, seems to be easy. But then, I cannot understand why so many do fail in their attempt".

Lord Kṛṣṇa: "Arjuna, constant thought – mental association of an object – produces an attachment or love in course of time, that leads to an all-consuming desire (kāma) to possess it. The obstacles that beset the path of its possession create anger (krodha). An angry person gets quite confused to know clearly what is good and what is bad. When he is thus blind to the good values of life, he is ruined (praṇaśyati). Thus, one's downfall and ruin come from wrong thought.

On the contrary, a Man of Perfect Wisdom, though surrounded by desirable objects is not affected by them. They cannot create in him any desire to possess them. He remains ever pure and peaceful. Because of his attitude of indifference – dispassion (vairāgya) to worldly objects – he knows no suffering, no pain.

As long as there is a clinging desire for earthly objects, there can never come true knowledge. He does not acquire the power of concentration. Consequently peace and happiness are strangers to him. The mind that covets and runs after worldly objects and worldly pleasures has no clear vision and is wrecked like a boat, tossed hither and thither in a stormy sea.

A Man of Perfect Knowledge sees everything clearly and there is nothing that he does not know. He knows what is real, the truth, and what is unreal, the false.

The ocean is always full. It does not crave for the continuous inflow of waters from the rivers. It does not undergo any change by the constant flowing in of waters from the rivers. In the same way, the Man of Perfect Wisdom does not cherish any desire for worldly objects. He is not disturbed in the least by them.[1] Desires may reach him from all

[1] आपूर्यमाणमचलप्रतिष्ठं समुद्रमापः प्रविशन्ति यद्वत् ।
तद्वत्कामा यं प्रविशन्ति सर्वे स शान्तिमाप्नोति न कामकामी ॥ २·७० ॥

*āpuryamāṇamacalapratiṣṭhaṁ samudramāpaḥ praviśanti yadvat,*
*tadvatkāmā yaṁ praviśanti sarve sa śāntimāpnoti na kāmakāmī.* (2.70)

2.70. He attains peace, into whom all desires enter as waters enter the ocean, which filled from all sides, remains unmoved; but not the 'desirer of desires'.

sides, but he never overflows into activities, just as the ocean never overflows although rivers flow into it and bring gallons of water.

The case is just the reverse in the man who harbours desires. Whether he fulfils them or not, he is always disturbed and ever uneasy. He and peace of mind are poles apart. Fulfilment of desires cannot bring peace and happiness. So, in order to attain this precious peace of mind, abandon all desires and the sense of 'I' and 'mine'. This attitude to life is the state of realisation of Brahman. Realise this, then there will be no more confusions. Just one glimpse of this highest state of Experience Divine is enough to free one from all agitations and their sufferings. It brings everlasting peace and happiness".

---

कार्पण्यदोषोपहतस्वभावः पृच्छामि त्वां धर्मसम्मूढचेताः ।
यच्छ्रेयः स्यान्निश्चितं ब्रूहि तन्मे शिष्यस्तेऽहं शाधि
मां त्वां प्रपन्नम् ॥२·७॥

*kārpaṇyadoṣopahatasvabhāvaḥ pṛcchāmi tvāṁ dharmasammūḍhacetāḥ,*
*yacchreyaḥ syānniścitaṁ brūhi tanme śiṣyaste'haṁ śādhi māṁ tvāṁ prapannam.* (2.7)

2.7. My heart is overpowered by the taint of pity; my mind is confused as to duty. I ask Thee. Tell me decisively what is good for me. I am Thy disciple. Instruct me who has taken refuge in Thee.

देहिनोऽस्मिन्यथा देहे कौमारं यौवनं जरा ।
तथा देहान्तरप्राप्तिर्धीरस्तत्र न मुह्यति ॥ २·१३ ॥

*dehino'sminyathā dehe kaumāraṁ yauvanaṁ jarā,*
*tathā dehāntaraprāptirdhīrastatra na muhyati.* (2.13)

2.13. Just as in this body, the embodied (soul) passes into childhood, youth, and old age, so also does he pass into another body.The firm man does not grieve at it.

स्वधर्ममपि चावेक्ष्य न विकम्पितुमर्हसि ।
धर्म्याद्धि युद्धाच्छ्रेयोऽन्यत्क्षत्रियस्य न विद्यते ॥ २·३१ ॥

*svadharmamapi cāvekṣya na vikampitumarhasi,*
*dharmyāddhi yuddhacchreyo'nyatkṣatriyasya na vidyate.* (2.31)

2.31. Further, looking at your own duty too, you should not waver, for there is nothing higher for a kṣatriya than a righteous war.

हतो वा प्राप्स्यसि स्वर्गं जित्वा वा भोक्ष्यसे महीम् ।
तस्मादुत्तिष्ठ कौन्तेय युद्धाय कृतनिश्चयः ॥ २·३७ ॥

*hato vā prāpsyasi svargaṁ jitvā vā bhokṣyase mahīm,*
*tasmāduttiṣṭha kaunteya yuddhāya kṛtaniścayaḥ.* (2.37)

2.37. Slain, you will obtain heaven; victorious, you will enjoy the earth; therefore, stand up, O son of Kuntī, with a resolve to fight.

नेहाभिक्रमनाशोऽस्ति प्रत्यवायो न विद्यते ।
स्वल्पमप्यस्य धर्मस्य त्रायते महतो भयात् ॥ २·४० ॥

*nehābhikramanāśo'sti pratyavāyo na vidyate,*
*svalpamapyasya dharmasya trāyate mahato bhayāt.* (2.40)

2.40. In this, there is no loss of effort nor is there any harm (production of contrary results). Even a little of this knowledge, even a little practice of this yoga, protects one from great fear.

प्रजहाति यदा कामान्सर्वान्पार्थ मनोगतान् ।
आत्मन्येवात्मना तुष्टः स्थितप्रज्ञस्तदोच्यते ॥ २·५५ ॥

*prajahāti yadā kāmānsarvānpārtha manogatān,*
*ātmanyevātmanā tuṣṭaḥ sthitaprajñastadocyate.* (2.55)

2.55. When a man completely casts off, O Pārtha, all the desires of the mind and is satisfied in the Self by the Self, then is he said to be One of Steady Wisdom.

विषया विनिवर्तन्ते निराहारस्य देहिनः ।
रसवर्जं रसोऽप्यस्य परं दृष्ट्वा निवर्तते ॥ २·५९॥

*viṣayā vinivartante nirāhārasya dehinaḥ,*
*rasavarjaṁ raso'pyasya paraṁ drṣṭvā nivartate.* (2.59)

2.59. The objects of the senses turn away from the abstinent man leaving the longing (behind); but his longing also turns away on seeing the Supreme.

ध्यायतो विषयान्पुंसः सङ्गस्तेषूपजायते ।
सङ्गात्सञ्जायते कामः कामात्क्रोधोऽभिजायते ॥ २·६२ ॥

*dhyāyato viṣayānpuṁsaḥ saṅgasteṣūpajāyate,*
*saṅgātsañjāyate kāmaḥ kāmātkrodho'bhijāyate.* (2.62)

2.62. When a man thinks of objects, attachment for them arises; from attachment desire is born; from desire arises anger.

क्रोधाद्भवति सम्मोहः सम्मोहात्स्मृतिविभ्रमः ।
स्मृतिभ्रंशाद् बुद्धिनाशो बुद्धिनाशात्प्रणश्यति ॥ २-६३ ॥

*krodhādbhavati sammohaḥ sammohātsmṛtivibhramaḥ,*
*smṛtibhraṁśād buddhināśo buddhināśātpraṇaśyati.* (2.63)

2.63. From anger comes delusion; from delusion loss of memory; from loss of memory the destruction of discrimination; from destruction of discrimination he perishes.

इन्द्रियाणां हि चरतां यन्मनोऽनुविधीयते ।
तदस्य हरति प्रज्ञां वायुर्नावमिवाम्भसि ॥ २-६७ ॥

*indriyāṇāṁ hi caratāṁ yanmano'nuvidhīyate,*
*tadasya harati prajñāṁ vāyurnāvamivāmbhasi.* (2.67)

2.67. For the mind, which follows in the wake of the wandering senses, carries away his discrimination, as the wind carries away a boat on the waters.

आपूर्यमाणमचलप्रतिष्ठं समुद्रमापः प्रविशन्ति यद्वत् ।
तद्वत्कामा यं प्रविशन्ति सर्वे स शान्तिमाप्नोति न
कामकामी ॥ २·७० ॥

*āpūryamāṇamacalapratiṣṭhaṁ samudramāpaḥ praviśanti yadvat,*
*tadvatkāmā yaṁ praviśanti sarve sa śāntimāpnoti na kāmakāmī.* (2.70)

2.70. He attains peace, into whom all desires enter as waters enter the ocean, which filled from all sides, remains unmoved; but not the 'desirer of desires'.

---

## Questions on Chapter 2

1 What did Kṛṣṇa say to Arjuna who was overcome with grief? (2-3)

2. What was the reply Arjuna gave to Lord Kṛṣṇa and how did Arjuna finally collapse after his hysterical outburst? (4-9)

3 Give an account of Kṛṣṇa's arguments to establish that the Ātman is indestructible and imperishable. (11-30)

4 What are the other points of view given in favour of fearless fight by Lord Kṛṣṇa? (31-38)

5 What do you understand by the buddhi-yoga given in *Gītā's* second chapter? (39-48)

6 What do they achieve, who are endowed with wisdom? (50-53)

7. How did Arjuna express his demand to know all about the nature of the Men of Wisdom? (54)

8 What are the features and habits of a sthitaprajña – a Man of Steady Wisdom? (55-61)

9 How does man perish because of his unintelligent contacts with the objects? (62-63)

10. Bring out clearly the difference in behaviour between the steady and the unsteady man, when they come in contact with the world outside. (64-69)

11. What is the Brāhmi-state? (70-72)

# Chapter III

## Karma-yoga

(Yoga of Action)

[Dedicated action, meaning of 'sacrifice' (yajña) of the vāsanās that are gathered by us as we live our life here and their tyranny upon us for years to come.]

Arjuna: "If, as you say, Kṛṣṇa, man of knowledge is really superior to the man of action, why do you advise me to pursue the path of action? Why do you urge me to take part in this dreadful war? I confess, I do not understand. Please tell me clearly, what I should do so that I may enjoy the supreme state".

Lord Kṛṣṇa: "A very sensible question indeed! See, Arjuna, there are two types of people – the purely intellectual and the physically active. The path of knowledge is prescribed for the intellectual, whereas the path of action is the best for the physically dynamic. But here, you must also understand that dedicated action is in itself not the final goal; it only paves the way for the final realisation of the Self. On the other hand, the path of wisdom takes one directly to the final goal".

Arjuna: "Again, you perplex me, Kṛṣṇa. Why should I not follow the direct and the easier path to reach the goal? Why should I fight at all?"

Lord Kṛṣṇa: "The path of knowledge is not the proper one for you, for the simple reason that you do not belong to the intellectual and the meditative type. As a prince (kṣatriya), your natural aptitude is for action.[1] You can satisfy and purify yourself only by action. The only course open to you is the discharge of your duty. Yes, your duties are to be discharged in a selfless spirit of pure devotion. Moreover, once you understand the art of selfless performance of duty, you are in the path of knowledge. These two 'paths'– the path of action and the path of knowledge – are not antagonistic but really complementary to each other".

---

[1] शौर्यं तेजो धृतिर्दाक्ष्यं युद्धे चाप्यपलायनम् ।
दानमीश्वरभावश्च क्षात्रं कर्म स्वभावजम् ॥ १८·४३ ॥

*śauryaṁ tejo dhṛtirdākṣyaṁ yuddhe cāpyapalāyanam,*
*dānamīśvarabhāvaśca kṣātraṁ karma svabhāvajam.* (18.43)

18.43. Prowess, splendour, firmness, dexterity and also not fleeing from battle, generosity, lordliness – these are the duties of the kṣatriyas, born of (their) own nature.

Arjuna: "Is not the performance of an action without any concern for the fruits thereof, the same as 'inaction' not doing it at all?"

Lord Kṛṣṇa: "What an absurd and foolish question Arjuna! An action done without any desire for the result is faultlessly perfect in performance. Such actions never produce any psychological reaction and so most wonderful results are gained through them. But inaction produces nothing. Inaction – running away from action is idleness. It does not bring perfection in man; it makes our minds dull, stupid and foul.

Moreover, all beings, consciously or unconsciously, are always active. Inaction goes against the laws of nature too. Besides, this abstention from action is only an external withdrawal of the sense organs from the objects. The mind would be always busy with passions and desires. So, this type of inaction, at best, is only self-deception or escapism. A real seeker of wisdom is the one, who conquers his organs of perception (jñāna indriyas) by his mind but launches his organs of action (karma indriyas) in the selfless discharge of his duty. Therefore, Arjuna, discharge your duty well. Performance of one's duty is, in all respects, preferable to utter 'inaction'. Nay, one cannot live even the ordinary everyday life, without doing anything; yes, one ruins even one's health by remaining idle.[1]

Arjuna: "But, Kṛṣṇa, ordinary actions entail bondages of vāsanās and drag us down to worldly imperfections and sufferings".

Lord Kṛṣṇa: "No, Arjuna, it is not so. As I said earlier, only those actions, which are prompted by desires chain us down, and not those performed in the discharge of one's duty, with, of course, no concern for the fruit and meant only as an offering at the feet of the Lord. Such an action is done really in the spirit of a yajña – a sacrifice – sacrificing our selfish desires for the welfare of humanity at large.

> [Meaning of the term 'yajña' – It is a word used to denote the Vaidika ritualism but the Lord extends its meaning to apply it for all selfless co-operative activities.]

---

[1] न हि देहभृता शक्यं त्यक्तुं कर्माण्यशेषतः ।
यस्तु कर्मफलत्यागी स त्यागीत्यभिधीयते ॥ १८-११ ॥

*na hi dehabhṛtā śakyaṁ tyaktuṁ karmāṇyaśeṣataḥ,*
*yastu karmaphalatyāgī sa tyāgītyabhidhīyate.* (18.11)

18.11. It is not possible for an embodied being to abandon actions entirely; but he who relinquishes 'the fruits of actions' is verily called a relinquisher (tyāgī).

In the beginning, Prajāpati, the Creator, created the living beings, along with a capacity for yajña in each of them. He blessed them and said, 'May you increase with 'sacrifice' (yajña). This 'sacrifice' does not mean, in this context, the kindling of fire, offering of ghee and other materials of worship and chanting of Vaidika mantras. The real import of 'sacrifice' is to work with a selfless attitude, in a spirit of dedication and wishing only for the common welfare. It is a co-operative, dedicated endeavour undertaken prayerfully, aiming at the happiness of all. The spirit of co-operation between the high and the low, between the rich and the poor, between the wise and the dull, and so on, spirit of 'give and take', the readiness of the 'haves' to share with the 'have nots' – all these and many more such divine and progressive values of harmonious living in society are meant by the word 'yajña'. But if one is ready only to take and not to give, he is verily a thief.[1] He commits the gravest and the most unpardonable crime. Can

[1] इष्टान्भोगान्हि वो देवा दास्यन्ते यज्ञभाविताः ।
तैर्दत्तानप्रदायैभ्यो यो भुङ्क्ते स्तेन एव सः ॥ ३·१२ ॥
*iṣṭānbhogānhi vo devā dāsyante yajñabhāvitāḥ,*
*tairdattānapradāyaibhyo yo bhuṅkte stena eva saḥ.* (3.12)

3.12. The devas, nourished by the sacrifice, will give you the desired objects. Indeed, he who enjoys objects given by the devas without offering (in return) to them, is verily a thief.

you mention any crime more sinful than this absence of co-operation in all social and national work and the spirit of sharing the results with all?

Look around and see Mother Nature at work. Does she not eloquently proclaim to us, in silence her spirit of constant sacrifice? The sun sheds light. The earth yields our needs. The fire gives heat. Do they ever ask us for anything in return?

Again, in the Vaidika period, we see plenty of this 'give and take' spirit. People propitiated the gods by sacrifice. The gods, pleased with their offerings, gave in return, rains. Rains made the earth fertile. The earth gave food. The people, nourished by this food became prosperous.

Thus you see, sacrifice is an unselfish action. Prosperity and plenty are the direct results of such dedicated actions. This dedicated action is, in fact, prompted by the good in us. This power to do has been given to us by the very Creator (Brahmā). The Creator is but the Supreme, manifested through its own creative urge. Thus, we get a glimpse of the highest Good (Brahman) in us in such unselfish actions. So, what we are bound to do in our station of life, we must do well, for our own good and for the good of the entire humanity. Wherever such noble work is undertaken by a team of workers in a spirit of co-operation (yajña) there is God, the Highest, manifest".

Arjuna: "Is this path, then to be pursued by all, Kṛṣṇa?"

Lord Kṛṣṇa: "No, not by all. Those who have already attained the highest perfect state need not. Since they have reached the highest state of eternal contentment, it is immaterial to them whether they act or abstain from actions. They have nothing to gain by actions either – for, in them, the individuality created by the ego, has ended. Therefore, they do not depend upon anyone for anything. They have gone beyond all these limitations.

But, Arjuna, your case is different. You are still a seeker of 'Knowledge'. You must discharge your duty in a spirit of dedication as an offering at My feet.

> [Kṛṣṇa cites the examples of such jñānīs (Men of Perfect Wisdom) who had attained perfection through selfless discharge of their duties.]

Janaka and other great kings attained perfection only by the strict observance of their duties. You should, Arjuna, follow the footsteps of those wise kings. Stand up. Conquer evil. Bring happiness and security to others.

Still, you do not look convinced of the truth of my arguments! Alright. Look at My life. From My very birth, I have been living a life of pure selfless service. Established as I am in the highest Knowledge, it is immaterial to me whether I act or remain idle. There is nothing to be gained or lost by Me by action or inaction. Still I am engaged in activities. Yes, even at this very moment am I not working as your charioteer?"

Arjuna: "I understand, Kṛṣṇa perfectly well your argument. Now as I came to think of it, why should you at all strain in such non-stop activities?"

Lord Kṛṣṇa: "Ah! there you have come to the core of the problem. The common people, endowed with average intelligence generally follow the great. Mostly they imitate the great. So, if I remain inactive, they also will remain inactive. They will just remain idle physically. Idleness, as we all know breeds indiscipline. I need not tell you the harmful effects of indiscipline.

Therefore, the wise as well as the ordinary man should be always engaged in activities. Just as the ordinary man diligently performs actions, prompted by his selfish motives, the wise also should do them equally diligently but selflessly, for the good of humanity.

I should warn, at this stage, the Men of Knowledge do desist from all attempts to advise the ignorant to improve them. It is true that they act, prompted by selfish motives. Advice given prematurely when they are not ready for it, or when they cannot understand its real import might probably prove disastrous. Why, they may even cease to act. Inaction, as I pointed out just now, ends in indiscipline. In order to avert this catastrophe, the wise should set an example by remaining in the path of action guided by the example before them".

Arjuna: "In what way, Kṛṣṇa, does the ignorant man get attached to action?"

Lord Kṛṣṇa: "The ignorance of the nature of the Self creates desires; desires generate thoughts;

thoughts produce actions. We, in our ignorance, due to our arrogant ego think that we perform, we accomplish, we succeed. Actually the actions are accomplished by the organs of action in us. But in our imperfect understanding we consider that we are the 'doers'. Therefore, we strive, we demand and, naturally, we get attached to the anxiety for enjoying the fruits of our actions. This is the story of our attachment to action.

But in the case of a wise man, who identifies himself with the Self and has gone beyond his ego sense, since the actions are not performed by the Self, he, the Self, cannot and does not claim the fruits of actions done by another, meaning, his organs of action.

The wise man should not confuse the ignorant one with these arguments; for, the latter would not understand".

Arjuna: "How can, then, an ignorant one like me, improve the standard of thought and come to understand the higher values of action?"

Lord Kṛṣṇa: "By dedicating yourself to the service of the world with pure selfless actions. In order to get less entangled with the world and its sufferings, offer all your actions, free from every selfish motive, at the feet of the Supreme. Such actions, purged of selfish motives and hopes are not done by the individual. The individual being is then, only a medium, through which the divine power manifests itself, through all its actions. Therefore, Arjuna, you can thus, become an instrument of the Supreme to work out His will.

My friend, dedicate yourself to the supreme Self, renouncing all your fears and anxieties regarding the outcome of war. Fight and discharge your duty. Those who perform actions in this unselfish spirit, with full faith in Me and My teachings are released forever from the bondages caused by action. The ignorant, however, who condemn My teachings and work to promote their selfish interests court their own downfall"[1].

[1] मच्चित्तः सर्वदुर्गाणि मत्प्रसादात्तरिष्यसि ।
अथ चेत्त्वमहङ्कारान्न श्रोष्यसि विनङ्क्ष्यसि ॥ १८.५८॥
*maccittaḥ sarvadurgāṇi matprasādāttariṣyasi,*
*atha cettvamahaṅkārānna śroṣyasi vinaṅkṣyasi.* (18.58)

18.58. Fixing your mind on Me, you shall, by My grace, overcome all obstacles; but if, from egoism, you will not hear Me, you shall perish.

[Vāsanās are the impressions brought over from previous births. These impressions order our intellect and we cannot pursue any path other than that ordered by the direction of our own present vāsanās.]

Arjuna: "Then, why do men reject this great and valuable truth and court their own downfall? Why can they not follow your teachings, discharge their duties well and gain happiness now and forever?"

Lord Kṛṣṇa: "Arjuna, when a being is born, he is born with certain latent impressions, tastes and inclinations. Instincts they are called, which he had acquired by his actions in his previous births. His present behaviour and attitude to life are mostly governed by his past actions (vāsanās). Even an honest seeker of the highest Truth acts, influenced by these impressions".

Arjuna: "Are not all of us, then, independent to follow your teachings, to improve, to perfect ourselves? If a man's present nature (vāsanā) is so powerful on him, as You say, do not Your teachings become practically useless?"

Lord Kṛṣṇa: "He can raise himself, if he masters his senses that produce attachment and hatred. He should try not to become a slave of his own senses. It is the senses that hurl him headlong into the hell of sufferings".

The mind, you must understand, is the playing ground of impressions (vāsanās). When we do not allow the impressions to multiply, which we can achieve with proper effort by giving up selfish actions altogether, the mind gradually becomes empty and the ego, the arrogant resident in the mind, ceases to exist. So, my friend, in whatever station of life you are placed, or find yourself to be in, discharge the duty in the manner prescribed, that is selfless, dedicated action with no anxious concern for the rewards thereof.

In this context, you must understand that no duty is superior or inferior to any other duty. Your duty is the best for you, for your own progress in your spiritual path. You can perfect yourself only by its strict observance. Even if death be the result one gets in the proper discharge of one's duty, well, accept it, embrace it wholeheartedly. Death, under this condition, is definitely better than any material gain promised by the discharge of another's duty[1].

Arjuna, a kṣatriya like you born to fight and rule will fail, if you were to take up the duty of a brāhmaṇa such as study, teaching and meditation.

Arjuna: "I find, even though one tries his best to run away from evil, O Kṛṣṇa! he cannot do so, sometimes. He is drawn, as it were, forcibly by an unseen power to commit sins".

Lord Kṛṣṇa: "Yes, it is true, to a certain extent. All beings have in themselves a dual personality. All of us have good and evil in us, found in varying proportions. When one's good nature prompts one to think good thoughts, to perform good actions, the evil nature pulls the same one into the opposite direction. This lower nature is otherwise termed as 'ignorance'. It breeds desires which in their wake create anger.

[1] श्रेयान्स्वधर्मो विगुणः परधर्मात्स्वनुष्ठितात् ।
स्वभावनियतं कर्म कुर्वन्नाप्नोति किल्बिषम् ॥ १८ · ४७ ॥
*śreyānsvadharmo viguṇaḥ paradharmātsvanuṣṭhītāt,*
*svabhavaniyataṁ karma kurvannāpnoti kilbiṣam.* (18.47)

18.47. Better is one's own duty (though) destitute of merits, than the duty of another well-performed. He who does the duty ordained by his own nature incurs no sin.

It is this vicious circle that does all the mischief in man.[1] Desire is at the root of all evils, and is our greatest enemy. We must conquer it. Just as smoke veils the all-bright fire, as dust veils the reflecting surface of a mirror and as the unborn child is covered by its mother's womb, so also desire veils the ever-pure Self, the all-illuminating Self-knowledge".

Arjuna: "What are the ways of attacking and destroying the desire-urges in us, which as you say, are our greatest enemy?"

Lord Kṛṣṇa: "This ruthless enemy – desire, resides in us carrying on its criminal activities with the help of the equipments of perception (jñāna indriyas) and the instruments of action (karma indriyas) at our mental and intellectual levels. Yes, the indisciplined and the unruly sense organs, the foolish and the arrogant mind, and the imperfectly trained intellect are the fields of action for desire. So our first attempt in discovering and destroying desire should be to check and control our disobedient senses. Then only the all-illumining perfect knowledge reveals itself to be experienced in our bosom as our own Self".

[1] Desire-attachment-actions beset with obstacles-anger, the friend and ally of the evil nature.

Arjuna: "Please tell me the secret strategy for the total conquest of all desires".

Lord Kṛṣṇa: "You see, man is made up of the physical body, the senses, the mind and the intellect. Beyond all these, the greatest principle of all, the pure Ātman, shines. Knowing thus the greatness of Ātman, identifying yourself with the ever-pure Self, Arjuna, conquer the dangerous devil, desire. In short, govern the mind by the intellect . Purify the intellect with meditation upon the Self, the Ātman (God) and with it, rule over the impure intellect. One who has become one with the Self, the Lord of lords, in Him all desires are completely at rest for ever".

---

श्रीभगवानुवाच
लोकेऽस्मिन्द्विविधा निष्ठा पुरा प्रोक्ता मयानघ ।
ज्ञानयोगेन साङ्ख्यानां कर्मयोगेन योगिनाम् ॥ ३·३ ॥

*śrībhagavānuvāca*
*loke'smindvividhā niṣṭhā purā proktā mayānagha,*
*jñānayogena sāṅkhyānāṁ karmayogena yoginām.* (3.3)

3.3. The Blessed Lord said: In this world there is a twofold path, as said before, O sinless one – The path of knowledge of sāṅkhyas and the path of action of the yogīs.

नियतं कुरु कर्म त्वं कर्म ज्यायो ह्यकर्मणः ।
शरीरयात्रापि च ते न प्रसिद्ध्येदकर्मणः ॥ ३·८ ॥

*niyataṁ kuru karma tvaṁ karma jyāyo hyakarmaṇaḥ,*
*śarīrayātrāpi ca te na prasiddhyedakarmaṇaḥ.* (3.8)

3.8. Perform (your) bounden duty, for, action is superior to inaction. Even the maintenance of the body would not be possible for you by inaction.

सहयज्ञाः प्रजाः सृष्ट्वा पुरोवाच प्रजापतिः ।
अनेन प्रसविष्यध्वमेष वोऽस्त्विष्टकामधुक् ॥ ३·१० ॥

*sahayajñāḥ pṛajāḥ sṛṣṭvā purovāca prajāpatiḥ,*
*anena prasaviṣyadhvameṣa vo'stviṣṭakāmadhuk.* (3.10)

10. The Prajāpati (the Creator) having in the beginning of creation, created mankind together with sacrifices said, 'By this, shall you prosper; let this be the milch cow of your desires, Kāmadhuk, (the cow which yields all desired objects)'.

इष्टान्भोगान्हि वो देवा दास्यन्ते यज्ञभाविताः ।
तैर्दत्तानप्रदायैभ्यो यो भुङ्क्ते स्तेन एव सः ॥ ३·१२ ॥

*iṣṭānbhogānhi vo devā dāsyante yajñabhāvitāḥ,*
*tairdattānapradāyaibhyo yo bhuṅkte stena eva saḥ.* (3.12)

12. The devas nourished by the sacrifice, will give you the desired objects. Indeed, he who enjoys objects given by the devas without offering (in return) to them, is verily a thief.

अन्नाद्भवन्ति भूतानि पर्जन्यादन्नसम्भवः ।
यज्ञाद्भवति पर्जन्यो यज्ञः कर्मसमुद्भवः ॥ ३·१४ ॥

*annādbhavanti bhūtāni parjanyādannasambhavaḥ,*
*yajñādbhavati parjanyo yajñaḥ karmasamudbhavaḥ.* (3.14)

3.14. From food come forth beings; from rain food is produced; from sacrifice arises rain, and sacrifice is born of action.

कर्म ब्रह्मोद्भवं विद्धि ब्रह्माक्षरसमुद्भवम् ।
तस्मात्सर्वगतं ब्रह्म नित्यं यज्ञे प्रतिष्ठितम् ॥ ३·१५ ॥

*karma brahmodbhavaṁ viddhi brahmākṣarasamudbhavam,*
*tasmātsarvagataṁ brahma nityaṁ yajñe pratiṣṭhitam.* (3.15)

3.15. Know you that action comes from Brahman and Brahman comes from the Imperishable. Therefore, the all-pervading Brahman (God) ever rests in sacrifice.

यद्यदाचरति श्रेष्ठस्तत्तदेवेतरो जनः ।
स यत्प्रमाणं कुरुते लोकस्तदनुवर्तते ॥ ३·२१ ॥

*yadyadācarati śreṣṭhastattadevetaro janaḥ,*
*sa yatpramāṇaṁ kurute lokastadanuvartate.* (3.21)

3.21. Whatever a great man does, that other men also do, (imitate); whatever he sets up as the standard, that the world (people) follows.

सक्ताः कर्मण्यविद्वांसो यथा कुर्वन्ति भारत ।
कुर्याद्विद्वांस्तथासक्तश्चिकीर्षुर्लोकसङ्ग्रहम् ॥ ३·२५ ॥

*saktāḥ karmaṇyavidvānso yathā kurvanti bhārata,*
*kuryādvidvanstathāsaktaścikīrṣurlokasaṅgraham.* (3.25)

3.25. As the ignorant men act from attachment to action, O Bhārata, so should the wise act without attachment, wishing the welfare of the world.

श्रेयान्स्वधर्मो विगुणः परधर्मात्स्वनुष्ठितात् ।
स्वधर्मे निधनं श्रेयः परधर्मो भयावहः ॥ ३·३५ ॥

*śreyānsvadharmo viguṇaḥ paradharmātsvanuṣṭhitāt,*
*svadharme nidhanaṁ śreyaḥ paradharmo bhayāvahaḥ.* (3.35)

3.35. Better is one's own 'duty', though devoid of merit than the 'duty' of another well discharged.

Better is death in one's own 'duty', the duty of another is fraught with fear (is productive of positive danger).

---

## Questions on Chapter III

1. What did Arjuna ask Kṛṣṇa when the latter explained to the Pāṇḍava prince about the brāhmi-sthiti? (1-2)

2. What does Lord Kṛṣṇa mean when he says that there are two ways of approach? (3)

3. How does Lord Kṛṣṇa prove that man is bound by action? (4-5)

4. Who is a hypocrite? (6)

5. How should we perform action? (7-9)

6. What is the ever revolving wheel of Life? (10-16)

7. Who are they that are exempted from performing actions? (17-18)

8. What are the arguments given for properly performing right actions? (19-26)

9. What is the logic of action or what is the philosophy of action? (27-28)

10. How can one be free from action? (29-32)

11. Where is the necessity to perform action according to our own nature? (33)

12. What are the two urges against which we must guard ourselves? (34)

13. How is it that one's own duty is to be performed and not that of others? Distinguish between svadharma and paradharma. (35)

14. What is that which propels a man to act in a particular way even if he does not wish to act that way? (37-39)

15. What is the strategy by which a desire, having entered the seat of our mind and intellect, brings disaster to the individual personality? (40)

16. How to destroy the inner enemy of man, the desire? (41-43)

# Chapter IV

## Jñāna-karma-sannyāsa-yoga

(Yoga of Renunciation of Action in Knowledge)

[Self-perfection – Division of humanity into four varṇas – brāhmaṇa, kṣatriya, vaiśya and śūdra.]

Lord Kṛṣṇa: "This knowledge of the Self, or rather the science of 'perfection' gained by pursuing the path of action, without attachment to the rewards thereof, is not a new discovery, but an ancient science, tested and proved to be quite scientific, logical, and rational. I declared it and taught it first to the Sun (vivasvān). The Sun taught Manu, the ancient lawgiver. Manu imparted this knowledge to Ikṣvāku, an old ancestor of the solar dynasty of kings. Handing down this knowledge from father to son, the ancient kings became proficient in it. That means, they practised what they learnt and obtained Liberation from worldly life, a life ruled by the passions and its consequent sufferings. This science, however, fell into disuse later on in the crowded life of thoughtless excitements polluted with the instinctive selfishness of man. You, being an ardent devotee of Mine and an eager student, and above all My friend, the essence of the same science is taught to you".

Arjuna: "Kṛṣṇa, how can I believe that you were the great seer and the first teacher of this science? The Sun was born in the beginning of the creation. Manu and Ikṣvāku were born long long ago. How did you, living now, come to teach them?"

Lord Kṛṣṇa: "Oh! Arjuna, this is not our first birth. Both of us have undergone many lives. But note the difference, I know them all, you know them not".

Arjuna: "All right. But you taught me that the knowledge of the Self removes the fear of the cycle of births and consequent agonies and you are proficient in the knowledge. Therefore, you are not, like the ignorant, tied down by the bondages (vāsanās) caused by actions. Then why have you taken birth at all?"

Lord Kṛṣṇa: "Arjuna, this is indeed a very sensible question. I am the Infinite, the Eternal and the Imperishable. Still I, out of My own free will assume a form and come to the world to establish dharma firmly, and to teach humanity to live a righteous life. I also put down evil[1].

Solely to protect the good (sadhu), to destroy the wicked (duṣkṛta) and to establish righteousness (dharma) I come into the world, assuming suitable form in every 'yuga'[2]. He who understands Me and the purpose of My incarnations, is in Me and he, at his death, merges into Me. Many have attained salvation in this way, consecrating their entire being in the acquisition of this perfect knowledge. They got themselves freed from all attachment, fear and anger. All seekers – whether they take to the path of action (karma) performing selfless actions, or to the path of

---

[1] यदा यदा हि धर्मस्य ग्लानिर्भवति भारत ।
अभ्युत्थानमधर्मस्य तदात्मानं सृजाम्यहम् ॥ ४·७ ॥
*yadā yadā hi dharmasya glānirbhavati bhārata,*
*abhyutthānamadharmasya tadātmānaṁ sṛjāmyaham.* (4.7)

4.7. Whenever there is decay of righteousness, O Bhārata, and rise of unrighteousness, then I manifest Myself.

[2] परित्राणाय साधूनां विनाशाय च दुष्कृताम् ।
धर्मसंस्थापनार्थाय सम्भवामि युगे युगे ॥ ४·८ ॥
*paritrāṇāya sādhūnāṁ vināśāya ca duṣkṛutām,*
*dharmasaṁsthāpanārthāya sambhavāmi yuge yuge.* (4.8)

4.8. For the protection of the good, for the destruction of the wicked and for the establishment of righteousness, I am born in every age.

devotion (bhakti), or to the path of knowledge (jñāna) – who, through understanding and meditation strive to reach the supreme Ideal, they all finally come to Me only.

Moreover, I am an impartial dispenser of rewards. In whatever form I am invoked and worshipped, in that form, I manifest Myself".

Arjuna: "If, as you say it is easy to gain the greatest reward, the highest knowledge, the perfection of the Self, why do so many pursue the lower paths and seek small material gains?"

Lord Kṛṣṇa: "Generally people take to the lower paths (sacrifices) because they want immediate rewards. They offer sacrifices, to please the gods and to gain immediate material rewards. In the spiritual path, the path leading to the realisation of the Spirit within, the progress is certainly slow and the reward not at all immediate.

> [The division and classification of castes, the types of mind-intellects available that constitute the humanity. The entire living creatures fall under these four types called varṇas.]

I have classified the people under four categories (1) brāhmaṇa (2) kṣatriya, (3)vaiśya and (4) śūdra, based on their tendencies (vāsanās) and actions[1]

[1] ब्राह्मणक्षत्रियविशां शूद्राणां च परंतप ।
कर्माणि प्रविभक्तानि स्वभावप्रभवैर्गुणैः ॥ १८·४१ ॥

*brāhmaṇakṣatriyaviśāṁ śūdrāṇāṁ ca parantapa,*
*karmāṇi pravibhaktāni svabhāvaprabhavairguṇaiḥ.* (18.41)

18.41. Of scholars (brāhmaṇas), leaders (kṣatriyas) and traders (vaiśyas), as also of workers (śūdras), O Parantapa, the duties are distributed according to the qualities born of their own nature.

शमो दमस्तपः शौचं क्षान्तिरार्जवमेव च ।
ज्ञानं विज्ञानमास्तिक्यं ब्रह्मकर्म स्वभावजम् ॥ १८·४२ ॥

*śamo damastapaḥ śaucaṁ kṣāntirārjavameva ca,*
*jñānaṁ vijñānamāstikyaṁ brahmakarma svabhāvajam.* (18.42)

18.42. Serenity, self-restraint, austerity, purity, forgiveness and also uprightness, knowledge, realisation and belief in God are the duties of the brāhmaṇas, born of (their own) nature.

शौर्यं तेजो धृतिर्दाक्ष्यं युद्धे चाप्यपलायनम् ।
दानमीश्वरभावश्च क्षात्रं कर्म स्वभावजम् ॥ १८·४३ ॥

*śauryaṁ tejo dhṛtirdākṣyaṁ yuddhe cāpyapalāyanam,*
*dānamīśvarabhāvaśca kṣātraṁ karma svabhāvajam.* (18.43)

18.43. Prowess, splendour, firmness, dexterity, and also not fleeing from battle, generosity, lordliness are the duties of the kṣatriyas, born of (their own) nature.

कृषिगौरक्ष्यवाणिज्यं वैश्यकर्म स्वभावजम् ।
परिचर्यात्मकं कर्म शूद्रस्यापि स्वभावजम् ॥ १८·४४ ॥

*kṛṣigaurakṣyavāṇijyaṁ vaiśyakarma svabhāvajam,*
*paricaryātmakaṁ karma śūdrasyāpi svabhāvajam.* (18.44)

18.44. Agriculture, cattle-rearing and trade are the duties of the vaiśyas, born of (their own) nature; and service is the duty of śūdras born of (their own) nature.

(karma), I allotted to them duties suited to their nature, to be performed by them to perfect themselves.

Brāhmaṇas, the meditative type are the best suited to study and to teach; kṣatriyas, physically strong and very active, to fight and to rule; vaiśyas to carry on trade; śūdras, to serve all people always. All over the world we can see these types always – the employers or commercial men (vaiśyas) and the employee-class (śūdras). I ordered these types according to the quality of thoughts and actions in each of these types.[1]

But I accomplish all these through My māyā-power. So I am not, in My absolute nature, the author of creation and of these classifications. Therefore, in Me there is no ego to claim the fruit of action. So no impressions cling to Me as I do not cling to the fruits of My actions. When you clearly understand the analysis of this secret of Mine, you too, will be freed for ever from all vāsanās.

[1] चातुर्वर्ण्यं मया सृष्टं गुणकर्मविभागशः ।
तस्य कर्तारमपि मां विद्ध्यकर्तारमव्ययम् ॥ ४·१३ ॥
*cāturvarṇyaṁ mayā sṛṣṭaṁ guṇakarmavibhāgaśaḥ,*
*tasya kartāramapi māṁ viddhyakartāramavyayam.* (4.13)

4.13. The fourfold varṇa has been created by Me according to the differentiation of guṇa and karma; though I am the author thereof, know Me as non-doer and immutable.

Now, do not think that this is a novel theory. It is not. This secret was understood by the ancient seekers. They pursued the path of the selfless service utterly indifferent to rewards. They became great seers of this Truth. Now, I advise you to follow the same path and succeed".

> [Karma – the right duty. How can one understand the right type of action as distinguished from the wrong type of actions? They seem to be very often indistinguishable to be judged easily.]

Arjuna: "All along you have been stressing on duty (karma). How am I to know, which is my right duty?"

Lord Kṛṣṇa: "Your doubt is quite natural and is certainly one to be expected. But Arjuna, you need not get too worried over this confusion. With regard to this question, regarding right duty (karma) and that forbidden by me (vikarma), even the great sages could not readily find a direct answer. It was a confusing problem even to them. The path of right action is very narrow. I shall teach you what is karma and what is vikarma, so that you will have no doubt as to your choice.

The question of karma has three aspects: (1) Performance of right action (karma) (2) Abstention from all actions (akarma) (3) Performance of forbidden actions (vikarma). We are not, of course, concerned here with the abstention from all actions (akarma), since without action, life cannot be. Wherever there is life there must be its manifestation, and the expressions of life through our organism, are our actions. True duty, right action is karma. Performance of correct action is always constructive and ever productive of good results. It helps one in one's own progress on the spiritual path.

On the other hand, performance of the forbidden actions (vikarma), is definitely destructive. It destroys the peace and poise in the one who is performing them, and brings about terrible sorrows and restlessness to others around him.

That man is the wisest, who, while doing actions, is not really doing them at all. He can remain as a passive spectator, an observer of the actions performed by his limbs. Thus his self, the individuality, detached from the vanity of doing things, is 'unactive', though his limbs are engaged in their actions.

So also, his self (individuality) can be equally active in 'unaction'. When his mind is busy in communion with God, holding an intimate interview with God – he is fully occupied within, while his limbs are not functioning at all in the world outside.

Thus, he can be 'inactive in action and active in inaction'. He is verily a saint. He intelligently conserves and concentrates all his energies on the action itself. He does not get disturbed and distracted by dreaming of the results.

Do not go with the idea that man, the theme of the philosophers, is just an inert piece of matter. No, he is the most dynamic force in the world.

The Self, being pure, remains ever pure, even though the body acts. No sin taints the Self as it does not do anything. It remains an unconcerned witness. A witness of a game cannot get tired and exhausted; the mad race is run by others, and the witness of it is but a mere onlooker".

Arjuna: "Please tell me more about this wise man".

Lord Kṛṣṇa: "He is perfectly content with what he gets. He is not elated or worried in success and failure, in joy and sorrow, by praise and censure, and in prosperity and adversity. He is calm and tranquil in all situations; conducive or unconducive. He has made a discovery of his perfection, which grants him infinite freedom. He is not chained any more to this limited and imperfect world of objects. He is thus established in the highest knowledge, the infinite wisdom. He does not run any more after the false attractions of the worthless world of things.

He considers all his worldly activities as offerings unto God. His actions are performed with such a deep devotion, goodwill and purity of mind that they are greater sacrifices than the ordinary religious rituals. Naturally, they bring forth better dividends.

Thus, when they pour out the best in them for humanity and to God, it is work and worship combined. The world at large is benefited and the Lord too is pleased with their actions. This is the greatest yajña, because both the world and God are pleased, whereas in the ordinary sacrificial rite, only God is invoked and propitiated.

When his limbs are active in the external world, his mind is kept in communion with God. This is the most healthy relationship between the body and the external world, and the mind and the supreme Lord.

The wise man is deaf and blind to the external world and to all its superficial attractions. He knows that the joy and the thrills that he would get from this world are only temporary. It would, at the end, leave but a feeling of regret that he has wasted his life. So he seeks the abiding happiness in selfless service in the constant remembrance of God.

Such actions do not chain him to the world and its agonies. He has no sense of doership as he knows that the Lord's will acts through him, rendering him incapable of doing anything wrong.

All those who are proficient in this science of sacrifice are qualified to reach the ideal goal, which indeed, is one and the same for all seekers. The inner satisfaction, the glow, the peace, the tranquility which one gets by such yajñas is the very essence of the bliss that is immortality. The reverse also is equally true. One who remains idle or performs but selfish actions knows no peace then or thereafter. These sacrifices are accomplished by self-effort alone. One who understands the essential truth of this science of life is fully equipped for his great pilgrimage to the freedom of God-state.

Knowledge alone can in the end take a person to the ultimate Reality. The path of knowledge is the highest, and it is the last stage in one's spiritual journey. All the other paths finally converge to this one main royal road to Truth. All the other paths are only various means to reach the path of knowledge, and this is the most direct, the most perfect way to the final goal. Once a man sets his foot on this path, he is literally at the very doors of Reality.

Arjuna: "What are the necessary requisites to acquire this supreme Knowledge?"

Lord Kṛṣṇa: "A learned teacher, who has intimate experience of Truth is certainly necessary. The disciple (śiśya) should have firm, unwavering faith in his teacher (Guru), and the student must surrender himself completely to his teacher. The śiśya should discuss his doubts with his Guru. Moreover, the seeker should live a pure life of self-control and devotion as prescribed by the teacher.

As in the case of other sciences, here, a mere objective understanding of the Truth is not enough. The teacher is efficient to teach only if he has intimate personal knowledge of the Experience Divine. However much you may study and understand the facts and theories in other branches of knowledge, you come to forget them in course of time. It is not so in the case of this science of Knowledge. Once learnt and experienced, it is gained for ever. There will be no confusion at all, whatsoever, on any point, at any time, regarding the nature of the Self.

When one is illumined by this Experience Divine, one will see that all beings, including oneself, are manifestations of the one supreme Self. This infinite Knowledge alone can remove completely our entire sins (vāsanās) and purify us".

Arjuna: "How can Knowledge remove one's sins?"

Lord Kṛṣṇa: "Just as fire burns and reduces any fuel to ashes, this Knowledge consumes all our actions – actions that create vāsanās – irrespective of their nature, both the sinful (pāpa) and the meritorious (puṇya). Even freshly cut firewood is reduced to ashes by fire, only it takes a longer time. So also the most heinous crimes will be burnt up by Knowledge. There is nothing in fact, more covetable; nothing more purifying than this all-purifying Knowledge. But you must not lose sight of the fact that only by constant and diligent self-effort, one can acquire this Knowledge. Even the teacher, who himself experiences this Knowledge cannot hand it over to his most intelligent student. He can only point out the 'way' to acquire it.

As in other branches of knowledge, one cannot set a time limit for the acquisition of this Knowledge. In spite of these drawbacks, I can say this much; strict adherence to the 'path' pursued, deep devotion to the ideal we have accepted and are striving to reach, self-restraint and constant endeavour are factors that would help to attain supreme peace (param śānti).

I warn you, Arjuna, that any one, who entertains even a shadow of doubt as to the importance of this Knowledge, or who has a faith, shaky and unsteady, is the most miserable man on this earth.

I assure you again and again that the one who releases himself from the senseless anxieties regarding the rewards of action (karmaphalam), and who has perfect faith in the divine statement that self-perfection can be achieved by the Knowledge, and who has the full mastery over the senses is a fulfilled jñānī – a Man of Wisdom.

He is liberated forever, even while alive (jīvanmukta). Now, Arjuna, my friend, are not you convinced? Get up; shake off your ignorance and put on the mantle of the knowledge of the Self".

---

ब्रह्मार्पणं ब्रह्म हविर्ब्रह्माग्नौ ब्रह्मणा हुतम् ।
ब्रह्मैव तेन गन्तव्यं ब्रह्मकर्मसमाधिना ॥ ४·२४ ॥

*brahmārpaṇaṁ brahma havirbrahmāgnau brahmaṇā hutam,*
*brahmāiva tena gantavyaṁ brahmakarmasamādhinā.* (4.24)

4.24. Brahman is the oblation; Brahman is the clarified butter and so on constituting the offerings, by Brahman is the oblation poured into the fire of Brahman; Brahman verily shall be reached by him who always sees Brahman in all actions.

तद्विद्धि प्रणिपातेन परिप्रश्नेन सेवया ।
उपदेक्ष्यन्ति ते ज्ञानं ज्ञानिनस्तत्त्वदर्शिनः ॥ ४·३४ ॥

*tadviddhi praṇipātena paripraśnena sevayā,*
*upadekṣyanti te jñānaṁ jñāninastattvadarśinaḥ.* (4.34)

4.34. Know that by obedience, by discussions and by service, the wise who have realised the Truth will instruct thee in (that) Knowledge.

---

## Questions on Chapter IV

1. What was the doubt that arose in Arjuna's mind and why? (2-4)
2. How did Kṛṣṇa help in explaining the matter? (5-8)
3. Who are those blessed souls who attain Liberation from the cycle of births and deaths? (9-12)
4. What is the fourfold varṇa system? Has this varṇa system any bearing upon our present casteism? (13)
5. How can we be free from the reactions when we are performing actions?(14-15)
6. What is the nature of true action? (16-17)

7. How does a karmayogī perform action? (18-23)

8. Enumerate the different kinds of sacrifices. (24-30)

9. 'To the non-performer of sacrifice this world is not'. What do you understand from this statement? (31)

10. How is 'knowledge-sacrifice' superior to the sacrifices for expected results? (33-38)

11. Who is the person fit to have this Knowledge? (39)

12. How does the man of doubting nature get himself doomed? (40)

13. What is the best way to act and at the same time be actionless? (41-42)

# Chapter V

## Karma-sannyāsa-yoga

(Yoga of True Renunciation of Action)

[Notwithstanding his arguments for the path of action, Kṛṣṇa had indicated now and then, that there is a nobler path, the path of renunciation.]

The path of renunciation and the path of action are, in effect, the same. The path of action is equally good as it teaches concentration and meditation, without which the last stage of the spiritual journey is impossible. Actions should be performed but not prompted and thereby, polluted by desires. By the single-minded concentration in doing selfless service, one grows within to be a sannyāsin. Such a contemplative mind readily progresses along the path of meditation and reaches the ideal. This efficient man, with all his sins washed off and free from any disturbance of pairs of opposites – success and failure, joy and sorrow, and so on comes to experience the true inner peace.]

Arjuna: "I am still in doubt, Kṛṣṇa, for you extolled the greatness of both the path of renunciation (sannyāsa-yoga) and the performance of actions (karma-yoga)".

Lord Kṛṣṇa: "Yes, Arjuna, renunciation as well as performance of actions both promise to take man to his spiritual goal and to provide inner freedom. Performance of actions, dedicated to the welfare of all, with no selfish motive, is far better than non-performance for a life of meditation. Pure meditation is impossible to one, who has not freely offered himself and what belongs to him, in the service of others.

Really speaking, one who accomplishes a total renunciation of his ego and thereafter performs selfless actions can be called a 'sannyāsin' for, he pours his entire self into his actions. This can be in the outer world of social work, or in the inner world, like a sage, intent on meditation upon God, undisturbed by joy and sorrow, praise and censure, and so on. A selfless worker who dedicates all his deeds unto Him is doing everything in the name of God, for God. He is also not disturbed by success and failure. He cultivates also a perfect mastery over his senses. Like the sage, he too, will come to enjoy infinite freedom, which is the State of Perfection.

The ignorant consider the path of renunciation (karma sannyāsa) and the path of action (yoga) as distinct and separate from each other. Actually there is no difference, and so there is no clash between the two paths. He who advances along the path of action will long find himself advancing along the path of renunciation. Both the paths serially lead to one and the same destination, and as such they are not parallel roads to truth, but the same royal road; the former section is named as the path of karma and the latter stretch of the same is named as the path of sannyāsa. The seekers start their pilgrimage from where they are – either from the former (the path of action) or from the latter (the path of renunciation) stretch of the road – according to their present state of progress. But understand, Arjuna, that those who see no difference in these two paths are those who are really wise; that which is the way of sannyāsa (renunciation) is itself way of yoga[1] (action).

---

[1] यत्साङ्ख्यैः प्राप्यते स्थानं तद्योगैरपि गम्यते ।
एकं साङ्ख्यं च योगं च यः पश्यति स पश्यति ॥ ५·५ ॥

*yatsāṅkhyaiḥ prāpyate sthānaṁ tadyogairapi gamyate,*
*ekaṁ sāṅkhyaṁ ca yogaṁ ca yaḥ paśyati sa paśyati.* (5-5)

5.5. That state which is attained by the sāṅkhyas (jñānīs) is reached by the yogins (karmayogins) as well. He 'sees', who 'sees' sāṅkhya and yoga as one.

Moreover, without offering selfless service in a yajña spirit, it is difficult to gain the true spirit of renunciation (sannyāsa). The performer of selfless actions (yogī) has the spirit of renunciation (sannyāsa) in him, because he renounces the desire for the rewards of his actions. So, whether one lives in this world, absorbed in selfless activities, or in the Himalayan caves in meditation, it amounts to the same. Either way, he is not bothered about the work done by the ears, eyes, nose, and so on. Hearing, seeing, smelling and so on are functions performed instinctively by the respective organs. Such diligent seekers are firmly rooted in their understanding that they are not doing anything by themselves. They live in the world untouched by the happenings around in the same way as the lotus leaves lie about in water. The lotus leaves are born in water; and exist always in water; yet they do not get wet. Similarly, Men of Perfection also remain untainted by their environments and actions in the world.

This attitude helps him to shake off all attachments and to perform all actions in the world with his body, mind and the intellect. He is thus purified, and he steadily perfects himself. He who has identified himself with the pure Self, stands aside, not contaminated by the effects of action (karmaphalam) and enjoys within, the eternal, infinite peace.

On the other hand those who are active, impelled by selfish motives and ever intent upon the results of their actions, are doomed by their own agitations and sorrows".

Arjuna: "Please explain the spirit of renunciation in more detail, Kṛṣṇa. It is becoming so very interesting".

Lord Kṛṣṇa: "Renunciation is not a mere giving up at the body level. Real renunciation comes when one renounces at the mental level also, never more harbouring any desire for the thing renounced. This is born out of intellectual conviction based on discrimination.

The ever pure Self is the sole master and the only resident living in all physical bodies. Unaffected, He watches the work done by the various instruments of perception (jñāna indriyas) and organs of action (karma indriyas) in the body. He does not himself do any work. Neither does He order the body, mind and intellect to perform their functions, nor does he also wish for the fruits of actions done by the 'ego' (jīva).

The divine Self does not ever give or take sin and merit. Thus, the Self enjoys serene and undisturbed peace. But, when the identification with matter (vāsanās) clouds the vision of the Self, it begins to think that it is the 'ego' (jīva), the doer and the experiencer. Naturally, it claims and clamours for the credit or moans and feels sorrows at the loss thereof. The pure infinite Self, you must understand, is not interested in the finite actions and in the resulting imperfect joys of the ego (jīva). This is the relationship between the Self (Ātman) and the 'ego' (jīva).

This Truth, being very subtle, is difficult to be understood by the ordinary man, who is under the impression, due to his ignorance (ajñāna) that he is the physical body equipped with a mind and intellect. This 'ignorance' (ajñānam) – the non-apprehension of Reality – disappears at the experience of 'Knowledge' (jñānam) – the apprehension of the Reality – just as the darkness is dissolved at the rise of the sun. Then the ego concept in us disappears and we come to live the nature of the infinite Self, the Divine, in our hearts.

[The spirit of equality and oneness alone is the boat to cross the saṁsāra. The final experience of a sannyāsin and a karmayogin is the same.]

When Knowledge shines forth in all its glory in the bosom of a sage, he realises that all are the play of the one Reality. The learned brāhmaṇa, the cow, the elephant, the dog, and the dog-eater are all various expressions of the same divinity. When the idea of separateness leaves him, that is, when he begins to see others as no other than his own Self, he is liberated forever. This wise man then experiences within his heart pure unbroken peace. He does neither jump about in his joys, nor does he sob in his sorrows.

Those who perform actions selflessly will ultimately come to experience the same infinite Bliss, just as that which is experienced by those absorbed in meditation, because both of them have left their 'ego', behind. In order to experience this infinite Bliss, one would conquer the 'ego' which is capable of experiencing only finite joys. So if you, Arjuna, want to experience this Bliss, it is possible to do so even now; provided you have the boldness and strength of mind to get away from the uneasiness and agitations arising from desire and anger. So, conquer desire and anger first.

That wise man, who thus realises the divinity of the Self and experiences the supreme joy of the

Self, is fully divine. It is thus, the common man with the dual personality of good and evil, that purifies himself and rises above his 'ego' through intelligent self-effort. He finds himself absolutely free to revel in the supreme Bliss of his own infinite freedom.

He finds all his happiness and fulfilment in his own tireless efforts at bringing about the enduring welfare of humanity. He himself is happy, and he loves to distribute as much of his happiness as he can to others. He finds his heaven[1] here itself among the members of the community, while he himself lives consistently an active and purposeful life of service to society.

> [A few important points on the path of meditation, the highest vocation in life, for which man alone is fit. Harmonising the thoughts and feelings, we discover the heart within, and to meet the peace infinite therein, is the art of meditation.]

I told you, in detail, how to get the power of meditation; practising single-minded concentration

---

[1] Not the heaven, as a special place, above the blue canopy of the sky, as described in the purāṇas where Indra rules, the apsarās dance and the gods drink the nector of immortality.

upon the performance of the right action. The essence of the process of meditation can be given in a nutshell. There should be perfect, loving, harmonious co-operation among the three aspects of a personality; the body, the mind and the intellect. The body knit together with the organs of perception and action should detach itself from the external objects, which give rise to the endless disturbance in the mind. Protected thus, from outer disturbances, the man of meditation should calm his mind slowly and steadily by breathing evenly. Sit, with the backbone erect, and concentrate on the infinite Lord. Detach the mind from desires, fear and anger, and direct the intellect to concentrate on the supreme goal. This is the method of meditation, where the body and the mind withdraw themselves from their respective functions, to help the intellect to concentrate powerfully upon the Lord of lords, the great friend of all. Meditation gives supreme joy and peace to the meditator throughout the day.

Do you need more details? Alright, I shall give you all the details in the following discourse, if you are ready to practise it regularly, daily and sincerely".

---

यत्साङ्ख्यैः प्राप्यते स्थानं तद्योगैरपि गम्यते ।
एकं साङ्ख्यं च योगं च यः पश्यति स पश्यति ॥ ५·५॥

*yatsāṅkhyaiḥ prāpyate sthānaṁ tadyogairapi gamyate,*
*ekaṁ sāṅkhyaṁ ca yogaṁ ca yaḥ paśyati sa paśyati.* (5.5)

5.5 That state which is attained by the sāṅkhyas (jñānīs) is reached by the yogins (karmayogins) as well. He 'sees', who 'sees' sāṅkhya and yoga as one.

विद्याविनयसम्पन्ने ब्राह्मणे गवि हस्तिनि ।
शुनि चैव श्वपाके च पण्डिताः समदर्शिनः ॥ ५·१८ ॥

*vidyāvinayasampanne brāhmaṇe gavi hastini,*
*śuni caiva śvapāke ca paṇḍitāḥ samadarśinaḥ.* (5.18)

5.18. Sages, because of their 'equal vision', treat all alike whether it is a brāhmaṇa endowed with learning and humility, a cow, an elephant, a dog or an outcaste.

---

## Questions on Chapter V

1. Explain Arjuna's difficulty in understanding karma-sannyāsa and karma-yoga? (l)

2. How does Lord Kṛṣṇa explain that the above two paths lead to the same goal and how does He prove that they are not two different paths but are

two different attitudes of the individual towards his work? (2-9)

3. How should one work so as not to be tainted by sin? (10-13)

4. What is the logic behind the statement that there is no action prescribed for the individual as such, and if at all he acts it is due to his nature? (14-15)

5. What is the way prescribed to get out of 'ignorance' with the help of Knowledge? (16-17)

6 What does the term 'samadarśana – equal vision' mean? (18-19)

7 What is the difference between enjoying sense objects and enjoying one's own Self? Which is superior and why? (20 - 28)

8 How is the sage, who has 'samadṛṣṭi', rewarded? (29)

# Chapter VI

## Dhyāna-yoga

(Yoga of Self Control / Meditation)

[Acquisition of supreme Knowledge Absolute by the pursuit of the path of meditation – the art of mastery of the mind. Here, we meet with all the technical know-how on how to unfold ourselves through meditation. What is not said here regarding meditation is not worth knowing.]

Lord Kṛṣṇa: "Dear Arjuna, you should not make the mistake of thinking that a householder, who gives up all sacrifices and the other duties enjoined on him, is a sannyāsī. You may now interrupt Me and say, 'Why, Kṛṣṇa, a sannyāsī also renounces these actions'. No, he does not renounce, he grows out of it all. A householder cannot renounce his duties, secular and sacred; for he has achieved or gained nothing worthwhile to renounce, he will only be an escapist, running away from his duties.

Sannyāsa means renunciation of all 'ego' and this is achieved through relinquishing – tyāga – the rewards of actions (karmaphalam). Sannyāsins and yogins are those who discharge their duties well in all the fields of social and human endeavour without demanding any credit for themselves. To them, work itself is worship – the service done is itself their reward and joy. A sannyāsī is also a yogī. Both of them are free from wishful thinking and useless fancying.

Sannyāsa and yoga are complementary to each other. Without the renunciation of the 'ego' (sannyāsa) to a certain extent, relinquishment of the anxieties to enjoy the fruits of action (yoga) is not possible. The renunciation of the fruits (tyāga) also requires renunciation of the 'ego' (sannyāsa). Both thus, go hand in hand; each is concurrent with the inherent in the other.

He, who wants to improve must work, either prompted by desires or otherwise. He may perform sacrifices as prescribed in the Vedas to please the Gods, seeking material gains. Slowly and gradually, he will come to realise that desireless deeds grant better dividends. So, he would begin to perform selfless actions.

At this stage, he can be called a sannyāsī and a yogī. He is not anxious any more to reap rewards, and hence a renouncer (sannyāsī), and as he is ever devoted to the service of Nārāyaṇa, a yogī too. Such a seeker can then walk easily on to the path of meditation, from where the full experience of the infinite Self is not difficult indeed.

In order to achieve this final goal – the Realisation of the supreme Lord – we should constantly and tirelessly strive. We can first improve and then perfect ourselves only by our own efforts. Understand Arjuna! we can bring about our own downfall by refusing to cast off our weakness, by refusing to improve ourselves by steady cultivation of the potential goodness in us. So, in effect, we alone are our own friends when we strive and struggle hard to develop the good in us, and we ourselves are our only enemies when we, in our idleness, refuse to strive in the self-unfolding path.

Since we have in us, both the good and the evil instincts, we must make an honest attempt to conquer the evil instincts by the good ones. We can never reach the ideal, if we refuse to cast off evil, our lower nature, and to accept the good, and improve it to shine the better. We must ever strive to outshine our own glory.

[Characteristics of a yogī: how can we understand that a person is really a yogī? How can we ourselves measure and know that we have improved ourselves?]

A yogī, who is in the path of perfection, finds that joy, sorrow, honour, dishonour, pleasure and pain do not disturb him at all. With the knowledge he has acquired from the immortal scriptures and also from the knowledge gained from his own personal experiences, he contemplates constantly upon the Lord – the Knowledge Absolute. He effectively withdraws his senses from the objects that please them, and successfully trains his mind to reject cravings for worldly things. He sees unity in the apparent diversity of the world around – such as, the worthless stone and the precious gold; the helpful friend and the injurious foe; the dear ones and the hateful ones; the relatives and strangers. He thus, discovers ever a soothing harmony enveloping him, both from within and from without. In short, he is in constant communion with God".

Arjuna: "Tell me, Kṛṣṇa, what are the necessary prerequisites for meditation – I mean, how are we to practise contemplation upon the Lord?"

Lord Kṛṣṇa: "That man, who is progressing in the path of perfection, and who does not want to be disturbed by what is happening in the world outside must, first of all, choose a solitary spot away from the crowd that might, in the beginning, disturb him. There, in a clean place, he should prepare a firm seat for meditation by spreading kuśa-grass on the ground. Over this, he should put a skin, and over that again spread a piece of clean cloth. He should sit erect on it in a comfortable posture, exercising perfect control over his body, senses and mind. Then he should direct his mind to think of God and God alone, with no other thought to disturb him. That is why I told you earlier that he should be in perfect harmony with himself as well as with the world outside. Then only, this single pointed concentration is possible. He should bring his mind back again to think of God whenever it runs wildly away, to think of other objects. He should sit erect and steady with head, neck and trunk in a straight line and then, as though gazing steadily in the direction of the tip of the nose, contemplate upon the Lord.

A serene and calm mind, fearlessness, physical and mental control (brahmacarya), moderation in food and sleep, and total concentration upon the Lord, are the factors that help one to succeed in meditation. He should practise moderation in his various and innumerable activities and recreations also. Overeating, fasting too much, oversleeping and keeping awake too long, destroy the depth and poise in meditation. If he observes sensible and intelligent moderation in all activities, he is fit to receive the highest Knowledge.

If a yogī in his exaggerated zeal to achieve the ideal, overindulges even in good activities, say, for example, charity (dāna), he will fail to achieve the infinite ideal. In this case, he will only realise his chosen ideal (charity), and he will miss the absolute goal and fall a victim to the lesser ideal, the sense of charity. In order to reach that finite ideal, he may start even sinful activities! Therefore, single-minded, faithful devotion to the path of meditation alone can give us that necessary meditative power to experience the highest Self, the Lord Infinite.

> [Definition of a yoga-yukta: whom do we accept as one who had achieved this great goal of all yoga? When can we consider ourselves as fulfilled in our quest?]

A master of his senses, free from all the cravings of the flesh and mind, a yoga-yukta, is one, who is in constant communion with God. He, through sincere efforts – physical, mental and intellectual – has completely erased all his evil instincts, leaving behind not even the traces of even one of them. He fully develops his good instincts to the maximum. He remains so steady in his contemplation that his mind in meditation can be compared to the steady flame of a candle burning in a place, undisturbed by breeze".

Arjuna: "Oh! Murāri, please also tell me the stages of progress in the path of meditation and the final state of yoga".

Lord Kṛṣṇa: "With a mind intelligently tamed and subdued and an intellect purified and sublimated to dwell in the glorious state of Godhood, one attains the realm of infinite bliss that can be appreciated and described only by such a refined sublime intellect. This infinite joy has no comparison whatsoever. No amount of finite joy gathered from the external world and added up can give us even a vague idea of the infinite joy of the yogī in meditation".

Once the yogī tastes this nectar of immortality, he becomes an addict to it. He clings on to it with a tenacity of purpose and determination. He never moves away from it. Detaching thus fully from the finite worldly joys, he attaches himself firmly and faithfully to this infinite Bliss – the state of Godhood.

From what I have said so far, Arjuna, please do not come to the conclusion that it is easy to soar into the heights of such perfect meditation. It is not a smooth flight. The progress from 'the starting point' to the 'finish' is very very slow, because there are innumerable obstacles, subtle as well as strong and challenges, powerful and frightening, all along the way. To overcome the obstacles and to face the challenges, the man, who wants to blossom into a yogī of meditation must have a firm willpower and a strong determination".

Arjuna: What all can be the obstacles and challenges, and how can we face them successfully, Kṛṣṇa?

Lord Kṛṣṇa: Arjuna, in spite of our intention to attain the goal, the mind by itself will gather from all sides, desires, which will then hamper our spiritual progress. By sheer force of determination, we should reject all desires, whatever be their nature. We should train our minds not to entertain any desires to possess and enjoy anything other than our great goal. When the mind gains a complete control over the senses, and the entire personality in an individual has only one noble dynamic desire – the desire to realise the Lord – he certainly meets no obstacles, and comes directly to experience the Self within.

The mind, thus made pure and sublime and entertaining only one desire – the desire for discovering the divine Self within – can be called the refined intellect. One should then train the intellect to constantly contemplate upon the Lord and the Lord alone.

The mind, thus made pure and sublime and trained is not conquered forever. It has a natural tendency to rush out and gather desires. So, whenever the mind wanders away from the noble idea of God, bring it back and tame it again. One should be always alert and vigilant to see that the mind does not stray away aimlessly from its determined point of attention.

Thus a yogī, by the practice of meditation, enjoys the infinite Bliss in meeting the Self. Bear in mind, Arjuna, that a perfect yogī has transcended his ego, and so has successfully eliminated his slavery to the endless demands of his body, mind and intellect. Do you not remember what I told you earlier that a yogī is a sannyāsī? He becomes divine".

**The Attitude of the Divine Yogī**

"He is divine and he sees the other beings also in the same light. He sees the essential divinity in them. He recognises the spark of glory in them and does not put any emphasis upon their bodies, their emotions or their intellects.

At the hour of God-experience, the Self meets only the Self and realises that everything is the manifestation of the Divine. Thereafter, he is not separated even for a moment from the Lord. He himself is divine and he sees and experiences only the fullness of divinity around him. Now, you would have understood, Arjuna, how a yogī comes to feel no difference between joy and sorrows, honour and disgrace, and so on. To him, whatever happens in the world is only an expression of the divinity in that form. He cannot see success as different from failure, because he sees in both the same hand of God".

Arjuna: "Inspite of your elaborate explanations, I fail to grasp the technique of contemplation. I would like to know how we can control the mind, which is now restless and is mad after worldly pleasures. I feel, it is easier to catch the wind blowing in all directions than to check a mind".

Lord Kṛṣṇa: "What you say is quite true. The mind is disobedient and is not at all available to listen to and profit by the helpful instructions given by the superior intellect.

But there are two unfailing methods by which we can fully control the mind, 'practice' (abhyāsa) and 'unattachment' (vairāgya).[1]

---

[1] श्रीभगवानुवाच
असंशयं महाबाहो मनो दुर्निग्रहं चलम् ।
अभ्यासेन तु कौन्तेय वैराग्येण च गृह्यते ॥ ६·३५॥

*śrībhagavānuvāca*
*asaṁśayaṁ mahabāho mano durnigrahaṁ calam,*
*abhyāsena tu kaunteya vairāgyeṇa ca gṛhyate.* (6.35)

6.35 The blessed Lord said: Undoubtedly, O mighty armed, the mind is difficult to control and is restless, but by practice, O son of Kuntī, and by dispassion it is restrained.

Constantly and repeatedly persuading back the mind from all its wanderings and training it to think of God, is 'practice' (abhyāsa). To leave off all attachments to the enjoyment of the world of objects outside is 'unattachment' (vairāgya). By this twin processes the mind can be finally broken and tamed. He alone gains the power of meditation, who can direct all his energies intelligently to reach the noble ideal set before him".

> [Yogabhraṣṭa – one who is self-exiled from the path of meditation. Some may fail on the path of yoga due to lack of mental control. But one must have put in a lot of efforts. Will this not be a wasted life of unproductive efforts?]

Arjuna: "All right Kṛṣṇa, but there must be people, who have struggled hard in the right direction to attain the ideal – constant contemplation upon and realisation of the Supreme – but have failed to attain it. It is also not due to their lack of faith in the ideal. It is mainly due to the restlessness of the mind, frivolous and frisking and fleeing from one desire to another, whichever refuses to be restrained for long. It demands intervals of recreation to roam about aimlessly in its usual fields of sense objects. The mind does thus sabotage man's efforts. What happens to such people? They have left the earth but have not reached heaven. They have lost their taste for the sense world but they have not gained the joys of the Self. Oh, Kṛṣṇa, You are the only teacher who can clear my doubts".

Lord Kṛṣṇa: "Arjuna, no one who has struggled at least a little to remain in the state of contemplation which leads to the realm of God; who has covered even a little distance in the pilgrimage and may not have reached the inner shrine, will ever come to ruin. How can a person with good and sincere intentions ever perish? Impossible.[1] The value of the reward depends on the intensity and the sincerity of his spiritual intentions; on the ardency and consistency with which he has pursued the path to reach the goal. The success in spiritual life is directly proportional to the right effort well spent with the proper attitude of true devotion in the heart.

[1] श्रीभगवानुवाच
पार्थ नैवेह नामुत्र विनाशस्तस्य विद्यते ।
न हि कल्याणकृत्कश्चिद्दुर्गतिं तात गच्छति ॥ ६.४० ॥
*śrībhagavānuvāca*
*pārtha naiveha nāmutra vināśastasya vidyate,*
*na hi kalyāṇakṛtkaściddurgatiṁ tāta gacchati.* (6.40)

6.40. The blessed Lord said: O Pārtha, neither in this world, nor in the next world is there destruction for him; none, verily, who strives to do good, O my son, ever comes to grief.

[The destiny of the yoga-bhraṣṭas – What happens to a yogī even if he fails on his path? Is it a calamitous tragedy, or only a temporary phase before his re-emergence?]

A seeker, a pilgrim on the great path, who is not steady in contemplation due to lack of self-control is called a yogabhraṣṭa, a self-exile from the path of meditation. Seekers practise meditation for some time but are compelled to leave it off later on due to the tyranny of some desire in them. This lack of self-control may arise from a desire to enjoy earthly pleasures or from a lack of physical and mental strength to stand the rigours of an austere life, or from an imperfect knowledge of the scriptures. There may be many other reasons. In all such cases, the great ambition to reach the state of steady contemplation was there always in their hearts. But due to some drawback in them they could not reach their ideal, though they honestly struggled. In such cases their efforts in that field will not certainly be wasted. They will be given suitable chances to reach their goal.

After death, they will first of all go to heaven and enjoy the pleasures there for years. They will then come back to the world again and will be born in such happy surroundings – wealthy, pure, wise, and so on, depending on their past tendencies (vāsanās) – wherein they can easily fulfil the mission that they had left off incomplete in their past birth; they will certainly continue it in this birth with more speed and determination because they are helped now by their spiritual strength acquired in the past".

Arjuna: "How can a yogabhraṣṭa, a self-exile from the path of meditation, bring his spiritual knowledge into the next birth?"

Lord Kṛṣṇa: "Just as today is only a continuation of yesterday and tomorrow is yesterday modified by the acts of today, the present birth is only a continuation of the past one and the next birth is determined and moulded by the present one. Just as a man continues his existence from one day to another, the soul, imperishable and eternal, continues its progress from one birth to another. Now, just as a man has an impression of the knowledge he acquired yesterday and other previous days, the yogabhraṣṭa also has the impression of the spiritual knowledge he acquired in past births. Just as a man accumulates knowledge of the world through days and months of his experiences, the one who is inclined to move along the spiritual path, collects it through births. A man takes up some work and finishes it in many days. So also the spiritually inclined man finishes his pilgrimage to the shrine of perfection in many births.

Therefore, when a yogabhraṣṭa starts his study of the scriptures he finds he can easily master the knowledge therein, because he started with a spiritual capital, already acquired in his past births. Moreover, he will be inclined to take to only the path of meditation as his previous practice in perfection goads him on.

Thus the yogabhraṣṭa, purified through a few births, blossoms into a perfect yogī.

Arjuna, my beloved child, understand well that it is the yogī who stands on the highest rung of the spiritual ladder. A man, perfect and steady in meditation is the noblest creature upon the earth. He is superior to sages, men of mere book knowledge (jñānīs) and men of selfless and dedicated actions (karmayogins). Meditation alone can take one to God. So Arjuna, be a yogī, come to identify with the infinite Reality, which is your essential nature.

Even among the yogins, those who can meditate upon Me effortlessly and with perfect faith are the best. They have already discovered their oneness with Me".

---

श्रीभगवानुवाच
असंशयं महाबाहो मनो दुर्निग्रहं चलम् ।
अभ्यासेन तु कौन्तेय वैराग्येण च गृह्यते ॥ ६·३५॥

*śrībhagavānuvāca*
*asaṁśayaṁ mahābāho mano durnigrahaṁ calam,*
*abhyāsena tu kaunteya vairāgyeṇa ca gṛhyate.* (6.35)

6.35 The blessed Lord said: Undoubtedly, O mighty armed, the mind is difficult to control and is restless; but by practice, O son of Kuntī, and by dispassion, it is restrained.

श्रीभगवानुवाच
पार्थ नैवेह नामुत्र विनाशस्तस्य विद्यते ।
न हि कल्याणकृत्कश्चिद्दुर्गतिं तात गच्छति ॥ ६·४०॥

*śrībhagavānuvāca*
*pārtha naiveha nāmutra vināśastasya vidyate,*
*na hi kalyāṇakṛtkaściddurgatiṁ tāta gacchati.* (6.40)

6.40. The blessed Lord said: O Pārtha, neither in this world, nor in the next world is there destruction for him; none, verily, who strives to do good, O my son, ever comes to grief.

अथवा योगिनामेव कुले भवति धीमताम् ।
एतद्धि दुर्लभतरं लोके जन्म यदीदृशम् ॥ ६·४२ ॥

*athavā yogināmeva kule bhavati dhīmatām,*
*etaddhi durlabhataraṁ loke janma yadīdṛśam.* (6.42)

6.42. Or, he is even born in the family of the wise yogīs; verily, a birth like this is very difficult to obtain in this world.

---

**Questions on Chapter VI**

1. How does Śrī Kṛṣṇa establish that sannyāsins and yogins are one and the same?, (1-4)
2. Explain in your words the statement that self alone is the friend and foe of oneself? (5-8)
3. How does a man of equable understanding – samabuddhi – grow in his excellence? (9)
4. Where is the necessity to be free from hopes and greed whenever a man wants to keep his mind steady? (10)

5. Elucidate the methods of keeping the mind steady. (11-15)
6. Who are all fit for the yoga of meditation? (16-18)
7. What will be the state of mind of one who has attained this yoga? (19-23)
8. Explain the technique by which the mind can be brought back, after it has contacted the known channels of disaster. (21-28)
9. What will be the attitude to life of an individual who is successful in dhyāna-yoga? (29-32)
10. How does Arjuna take the statement that mind must be controlled? (33-34)
11. What happens to seekers who do not succeed in this life while on this path? (40)
12. Is any 'fall' possible in the path of perfection and if so, how can a man come up again? (41-44)
13. Who is said to be the greatest yogin among the other types of seekers? (45-47)

# Chapter VII

## Jñāna-vijñāna-yoga

(Yoga of Knowledge & Wisdom)

[Knowledge and wisdom – meaning the intellectual understanding and intimate experience. The knowledge acquired through theoretical studies and the knowledge acquired through personal experiences. The former is raw knowledge, and the latter is true wisdom.

The knowledge of the Self, seemingly so stupendous is made so clear and simple by Kṛṣṇa that even our limited intellect can understand the infinite Self in all its relative aspects. This knowledge of the Reality cannot be grasped by those enveloped by sattva, rajas and tamas, constituting ignorance, but certainly it can be grasped by those, who struggle hard, may be through many births, and those who sublimate themselves by casting off their sense of duality. The Lord had already taught Arjuna the art of meditation, and now it is taken for granted that the student has understood it. So here, He is talking to that one who has already mastered the method of meditation.]

Arjuna : "After acquiring this power of meditation, I know I must fix my mind upon You, the supreme Lord of all. So what is Your real nature, Kṛṣṇa? Tell me all that I should know".

Lord Kṛṣṇa: "Yes, I shall not only give you the theoretical knowledge but I shall also advise you on the technique of practical application. When you learn the theory and then realise Me working upon that knowledge, understand that there is nothing more to be known.

Among thousands of people, you may find just one, who seeks spiritual knowledge. Among thousands of such seekers, there may be just one who knows Me well. The seekers are few indeed; but remember, the seers are fewer still.

I have two aspects, as it were. My lower nature (aparā prakṛti) and My higher nature (parā prakṛti). My lower nature appears in eight forms. They are earth (pṛthvi); water (āpa); fire (tejasa); air (vāyu);

space (ākāśa or khaṁ); mind (manas); intellect (buddhi) and egoism (ahaṅkāra).

The higher and the pure nature is, concisely speaking, the fundamental factor, the foundation, the substratum, the very life-breath, the very essence of everything – the Ātman, the Self.

We shall call the lower as 'matter' (prakṛti) and the higher as 'Spirit' (puruṣa). You must realise that this universe has sprung from these two natures only.

[What exactly is this higher nature of the Lord? Where can we meet this pure expression of the Lord? How can we recognise it?]

In my higher nature, I am the sole seed of everything. There is nothing which is higher or beyond Me. In short, I am the subtle Truth that runs through all, and that holds the world of beings together. Metaphorically speaking, I am the one essence running through everything, holding them together into this world pattern, as the string keeps the pearls together in a necklace. To make the same idea clearer I tell you that I am the fluidity in water, the light in the sun and moon, the mystic and the sacred symbol 'Om' of the scriptures, the sound in ether, manliness in man, fragrance in earth, the heat in the fire, the life-breath in all living creatures, the penance in the sages, the intelligence in the intelligent, the efficiency in the clever, the physical strength devoid of desire and attachment in the powerful, the lawful desire in all beings and so on. Yes, I am the all sustaining and ever surviving substratum of everything".

Arjuna: "If you are the Spirit, the life-giving pure essence in everything, why should You take refuge, as it were, in the base and impure body, which is nothing but matter?"

Lord Kṛṣṇa: "Please understand Arjuna, that I embrace matter only to express Myself, My glory, My strength, My greatness. All the beings, the pure, the active and the inert are My own creations. I guide them. They do not guide Me. I do not take refuge in them. They take refuge in Me. The naked eye must necessarily see the Spirit encaged, imprisoned in matter. But when the vision is improved by the lens of Knowledge, we will see that the Spirit envelops everything. Matter depends upon the Spirit. The Spirit does not depend upon matter".

Arjuna: "If it is so, then why can't people understand or at least recognise this great Truth and live upon it?"

Lord Kṛṣṇa: "In all beings, we find, in varying proportions, the three guṇas – pure attitude (sattva), active attitude (rajas) and inert attitude (tamas). These together constitute ignorance (avidyā). So due to the three guṇas, the whole world is deluded and ignorant. Due to this delusion or total ignorance (māyā) men fail to recognise the eternal, imperishable Me – the Spirit – as distinct from the gross base matter".

Arjuna: "Tell me more about this delusion, its nature and how it is caused".

Lord Kṛṣṇa: "This ignorance or delusion is, in a way, caused by Me. It is, as I told you just now, pure (sattva), active (rajas), and inert (tamas) elements in man's thought personality.

It is very difficult to dispel this darkness of ignorance and get enlightened. But do not get discouraged. Those who take refuge in Me can certainly overcome it.

The evil doers, the sinners deluded by māyā, do not seek Me at all. Their power to distinguish, to discriminate between right and wrong is almost zero. So they generally follow the wrong path.

> [The seekers of the Spirit - the pilgrims to the shrine of the Spirit. Who are those that strive sincerely to break the limitations of matter and reach the shores of the Spirit?]

The good ones, who take refuge in Me can be classified under four heads:

1. The tormented and the tortured by the sufferings in the world (ārta);
2. The lovers of the knowledge of the Spirit (jigñāsu);
3. Seekers after worldly riches (arthārthī); and
4. The wise seeking the Spirit (jñānī).

Of these, the wise ones, firm in meditation and extremely devoted to Me, are superior to the first three types. They love Me, I love them. They are dearest to Me".

Arjuna: "Then do You condemn the other three types?"

Lord Kṛṣṇa: "No, Arjuna, certainly not. All these are indeed noble. But the wise man (jñānī) comes the quickest to Me, because he advances in the light of 'Knowledge', whereas the others totter along in the darkness of ignorance. The former has shed his ego completely. He is My very special favourite, nay, My own self. Remember this Arjuna, that even the wise can accomplish the divine pilgrimage only after many births. In the full ripeness alone he can realise the pure Spirit, who is Vāsudeva. Such souls are rare to be found in life.

[Sincere seekers certainly see Me.]

To an average man of the world, desire is his god in life, and the fulfilment of any desire means the propitiation of that deity. Ordinarily, the desires are many and varied. Then it comes to this. An average man has to propitiate as many deities as there are desires. He, therefore, wastes all his energies in the fulfilment of all these desires. What does he get in return? Only material perishable rewards, and when they perish his sorrows start!

So, if a seeker's sole, single desire is Self-fulfilment, Self-perfection, Self-realisation, it becomes evident that he should direct all his energies into the one channel of settling the Lord in the heart, the Ātman. With determination, he must toil along and whatever be the obstacles en route, he should steadily surmount them and must strive steadily to reach the destination. Here also, the desire, the deity, the great Self in him will pull him forward on his march, till he reaches to become one with the pure Ātman.

Now understand this fundamental fact, Arjuna, 'What you think, so you become'. Your pattern of thought moulds you. So have only one noble sublime thought – the constant thought of the living Lord.

Ignoble and impure thoughts are also generated by Me by My māyā. It is I, who gives the deserving fruits of such thoughts and their resultant actions. Bear in mind that this fruit is not good and sweet at all, whereas the fruit of the God thought is immortal. So you must remove the veil of māyā and see My glory and come to revel in that Glory Eternal.

You may ask now, 'Why do men, as a rule turn away from the enjoyment of that infinite glory?' The man of the world with average intelligence gets confused in the notion that the pure all-pervading Principle, My higher nature, is the same as the impure, limited gross matter, perceived so readily in different forms. The former is Me, the One; the latter is again Me, the many. The former is unmanifest but definitely present in everyone; the latter is manifest in the world of plurality. The former cannot be directly seen to exist by your organs of perception, but can be realised, and that too, only with the refined and sublime intellect. In short, the many forms of matter can be seen, but one form of the Spirit can only be experienced. This general ignorance and the consequent confusions are caused by my māyā, a veil of total ignorance of My true nature, springing from the guṇas (sattva, rajas and tamas) and hence the common man fails to realise Me. With his common gross intellect he cannot lift the veil of ignorance (ajñāna), while for a sincere seeker, endowed with the uncommon, refined and penetrating intellect, the veil does not exist at all.

Any worldly desire, in its progress from its very inception to its fulfilment, has to face obstacles, which breed only disturbances in the mind. How can a disturbed mind see anything, even a finite object in its true value or perspective, let alone the infinite Me?

[Hence it is left to the seeker to avoid all desires and the consequent conflicts and disturbances of the mind, and finally escape from this devastating, destructive and dangerous delusion. What then are the qualifications of a sincere seeker? What are his motives?]

A sincere seeker is one, who, in the face of obstacles on the path of Realisation does not get discouraged and desperate. He does not turn back but moves forward slowly and steadily, very carefully avoiding the pitfalls of desires and the resulting vāsanās, which will breed only more desires and more vāsanās, thus binding him more and more to the world. He ever strives to exhaust even his existing vāsanās by performing selfless actions.

These sincere seekers, freed from sins come out of the evil of ignorance and truly worship me.

The main motive of these seekers is to release themselves from the agonies of birth and death. They know that I alone can liberate them. Thus, the wise man comes to realise that the Self in him is the very foundation of the whole universe. The Self is the most dynamic spark, capable of changing the face of the entire universe, which, in effect, is only another form of the one Self appearing in a multitude of forms.

He develops the divinity in him, and expands himself to comprehend the vast universe, with all its multiplicity of forms, as only an offshoot of the Paramātman. The real knowledge is the knowledge that the Self, the eternal Principle, is one and the same, and is the foundation of all actions – worldly (adhibhūtaṁ) and spiritual (adhiyajñaṁ); the life spark, the essence in all beings; – in human beings as the Self (adhyātmam) and in the cosmos as the divine (adhidaivam) – the ultimate essence common in matter and Spirit".

---

रसोऽहमप्सु कौन्तेय प्रभास्मि शशिसूर्ययोः ।
प्रणवः सर्ववेदेषु शब्दः खे पौरुषं नृषु ॥ ७.८ ॥

*raso'hamapsu kaunteya prabhāsmi śaśisūryayoḥ,*
*praṇavaḥ sarvavedeṣu śabdaḥ khe pauruṣaṁ nṛṣu.* (7.8)

7.8. I am the sapidity in water, O son of Kuntī, I am the light in the moon and the sun; I am the syllable Om in all the Vedas, sound in ether and virility in men.

पुण्यो गन्धः पृथिव्यां च तेजश्चास्मि विभावसौ ।
जीवनं सर्वभूतेषु तपश्चास्मि तपस्विषु ॥ ७·९ ॥

*puṇyo gandhaḥ pṛthivyāṁ ca tejaścāsmi vibhāvasau,*
*jīvanaṁ sarvabhuteṣu tapaścāsmi tapasviṣu.* (7.9)

7.9. I am the sweet fragrance in earth and the brilliance in the fire, the life in all beings, and I am austerity in the austere.

बीजं मां सर्वभूतानां विद्धि पार्थ सनातनम् ।
बुद्धिर्बुद्धिमतामस्मि तेजस्तेजस्विनामहम् ॥ ७·१० ॥

*bījaṁ māṁ sarvabhūtānāṁ viddhi pārtha sanātanam,*
*buddhirbuddhimatāmasmi tejastejasvināmaham.* (7.10)

7.10. Know Me, O Pārtha, as the eternal seed of all beings; I am the intelligence of the intelligent. The splendour of the splendid (things and beings), am I.

बलं बलवतां चाहं कामरागविवर्जितम् ।
धर्माविरुद्धो भूतेषु कामोऽस्मि भरतर्षभ ॥ ७·११ ॥

*balaṁ balavatāṁ cāhaṁ kāmarāgavivarjitam,*
*dharmāviruddho bhūteṣu kāmo'smi bharatarṣabha.* (7.11)

7.11. Of the strong, I am the strength, devoid of desire and attachment; and in (all) beings, I am the desire, unopposed to dharma, O best among the Bharatas.

दैवी ह्येषा गुणमयी मम माया दुरत्यया ।
मामेव ये प्रपद्यन्ते मायामेतां तरन्ति ते ॥ ७-१४ ॥

*daivī hyeṣā guṇamayī mama māyā duratyayā,*
*māmeva ye prapadyante māyāmetāṁ taranti te.* (7.14)

7.14. Verily, this divine illusion of Mine, made up of guṇas (caused by the qualities) is difficult to cross over; those who take refuge in Me, alone come to cross over this illusion.

---

## Questions on Chapter VII

1. What is the yoga that Kṛṣṇa taught in the seventh chapter? What is the greatness of this yoga? (1-3)

2. What do you know about the eightfold division of prakṛti? (4)

3. What is it that Lord Kṛṣṇa indicates as His 'superior prakṛti', superior nature? (5)

4. What is the relationship between the Lord and prakṛti manifested as the universe? (6)

5. How does Lord Kṛṣṇa explain this relationship (with examples)? (7-12)

6. How is it that men are not aware of this substratum and what is the way to come out of this delusion? (13-14)

7. Who are said to be of demonic tendencies and why? (15)
8. Who are the four types of worshippers? (16)
9. How does Lord Kṛṣṇa assess them according to their order of merit? (17-24)
10. What is yoga-māyā? (25)
11. What is that by which the beings are subjected to this yoga-māyā (illusion divine)? (27)
12. Who are those blessed souls who cross over this yoga-māyā and attain Self-realisation? (28-30)

# Chapter VIII

## Akṣara-brahma-yoga

(Yoga of Imperishable Brahman)

[The man of wisdom (jñānī) is able to distinguish between the lower and higher natures of the Lord, and to identify himself with the higher. He also moves at will in the fields of his lower manifestations. He never makes any wrong contact with the outside world and never invites sufferings. He is quite at home and contented wherever he is and in whatever situation he finds himself in. His wisdom can fully comprehend that from the highest and the most dynamic Lord to the lowest inert stone. All are the expressions of the divine Light – the pure Consciousness – in everyone of us.

The final release from the agonies of worldly existence, necessary for the purification and sublimation of his intellect so that he can fix it on the Lord within, can be effected only by the withdrawal of all the sense organs from the objects of the outside world.]

Arjuna: "Kṛṣṇa, You have introduced many new expressions such as adhyātma, adhibhūta, adhidaiva and adhiyajña. Please fully explain them to me. Tell me also about Brahman and karma. How can a self-controlled man realise You at death?"

Lord Kṛṣṇa: "Brahman is the Lord Himself, imperishable and supreme, the sole source of the entire universe.

Karma is the creative strength behind every active intellect, fulfilling itself in creation.

Adhyātma is He; the supreme Self, the common subtle Principle, that graces all bodies as the Ātman, the Self.

Adhibhūta is the manifested universe as contrasted with the imperishable unmanifest Lord.

Adhidaiva is the imperishable Puruṣa, the indweller in everything. He is the presiding deity in all, manifesting His presence and power through the organs of perception and the organs of action.

Adhiyajña am I, who am also the invisible Spirit behind all selfless actions, performed in the yajña spirit.

You should not get perplexed at this variety of expressions employed in describing Me because, all these in essence, give but one and the same idea. They denote that the eternal Self alone is real and all the rest are ignorant superimpositions upon It. The knowledge of the Self is the knowledge of everything and when one attains that knowledge, he is free to act or not to act wherever he chooses to be in the manifest fields of existence. This gives also the final release from the agonies of worldly existence.

One who understands that the body is only a field for the Self to play in, aspires to reach the Reality through the visible play of the Lord. At death, he leaves the body meditating on Me alone and this final thought, constant in the last stage of life decides his future destiny.

Since the time of death is uncertain and unknown, you should train your mind to meditate always on the eternal Lord, to the exclusion of all other thoughts. It is guaranteed that you would reach the destination – Me, the Puruṣa – successfully.

[What are the characteristics of this Spirit – the Puruṣa? How can we detect its presence? If there is any secret technique, what exactly is it?]

Of course, no one can give in full an exhaustive explanation of the nature of the Puruṣa. I can only indicate a few.

The Puruṣa knows all the past, the present and the future as it is the Knowledge. He is the most ancient one, in existence even before the beginning of time, and which no intellect can reach. He is the sole sovereign of the entire universe. He is subtler than the subtlest things known to us. He is the foundation, the sole substratum, the supporting factor of all. His form cannot be conceived by any intellect. He is pure effulgence, like the sun. He is beyond the darkness of ignorance.

With the equipments of perception and knowledge, limited as they are in their scope, the Puruṣa, the unlimited Reality, cannot be fully comprehended. But one who wakes up from this false, unreal, worldly existence, can certainly comprehend the Puruṣa in His real nature.

At the utter annihilation of the ego, the pure intellect, endowed with the strength of contemplation can concentrate all its attention and energies on the Puruṣa. This divine peaceful thought acts like a bridge for the pure intellect to cross over its own limitations. The greater the intensity of thought, the shorter is the length of the bridge. The thought crawls forward to the Puruṣa and the Puruṣa attracts it towards Himself. Thus mutually gravitating towards each other, in the end, the thought and the Puruṣa become one Experience Supreme".

Arjuna: "Describe to me this glorious realm of oneness with the Puruṣa!"

Lord Kṛṣṇa: "This is that glorious realm, proclaimed in the Upaniṣads as imperishable, where the sages, freed from desire, go and for reaching which brahmacarya (physical and mental discipline) is practised. It can be reached in two steps: (1) first through the intelligent control over the body, the sense organs, the mind and the gross intellect which means raising oneself above the physical, mental and intellectual realm and their disturbances; (2) by constant contemplation, with all the intensity the higher intellect can mobilise and bring forth. To put it concisely, we can realise the Self by detaching completely from 'here' and by attaching fully to 'there'.

The sacred symbol 'Om' represents Brahman, the transcendental. One who meditates with intense concentration upon 'Om' knowing its full significance, reaches out to revel in the glorious realm where pure soothing silence reigns. It is accessible only to those yogins, who are steady in their contemplation.

The benefit that is promised to those reaching this realm is the final release from rebirth and its attendant agonies.

> [No one, not even the Creator, is free from rebirth. But once a yogin reaches Me, he stays with Me forever. What is creation and what exactly is dissolution? Who creates and when? Why this dissolution and how? What are the benefits of this Self-realisation?]

God's day is man's year; in short, a divine day is a human year. Twelve thousand divine years are equal to one caturyuga[1]; one thousand such caturyugas constitute one day (12 hours) for Brahmā, the Creator. Brahma's night is another one thousand 'caturyugas'. Creation starts at the dawn of the Creator's day and continues till his evening without break. The entire changing universe of manifested matter springs from the single unmanifest Lord at the dawn.

The Creator stops his work of creation, at the approach of his night, and the created worlds get dissolved or absorbed into himself. The manifest beings are helpless victims of this unending process of birth and death .

Beyond all these manifest and unmanifest, and ever running through them is that imperishable Reality, the foundation and the substratum of everything.[2]

---

[1] Four Yugas - Kṛta, Treta, Dvāpara and Kali.

[2] उत्तमः पुरुषस्त्वन्यः परमात्मेत्युदाहृतः ।
यो लोकत्रयमाविश्य बिभर्त्यव्यय ईश्वरः ॥ १५·१७ ॥
*uttamaḥ puruṣastvanyaḥ paramātmetyudāhṛtaḥ,*
*yo lokatrayamāviśya bibhartyavyaya īśvaraḥ.* (15.17)

15.17 But distinct is the supreme Puruṣa called the highest Self, the indestructible Lord, who pervading the three worlds (waking, dream and deep sleep), sustains them.

This is the realm of the Spirit, the changeless Puruṣa and is the highest and the final goal of all beings. Those who reach this realm never return.[1]

One who knows what has been said here, never commits any mistake in his spiritual efforts and never fails. He is sure to reach and revel in My realm. So Arjuna, always aspire for this great grand experience.

Such a yogin meditating upon the imperishable Brahman (the almighty God) with a steady mind and firm faith reaches that glorious realm and obtains greater rewards than any scholar of Vedānta or sacrificer or recluse".

---

ओमित्येकाक्षरं ब्रह्म व्याहरन्मामनुस्मरन् ।
यः प्रयाति त्यजन्देहं स याति परमां गतिम् ॥ ८·१३ ॥

---

[1] न तद्भासयते सूर्यो न शशाङ्को न पावकः ।
यद्गत्वा न निवर्तन्ते तद्धाम परमं मम ॥ १५·६ ॥
*na tadbhāsayate sūryo na śaśāṅko na pāvakah,*
*yadgatvā na nivartante taddhāma paramaṁ mama.* (15.6)

15.6 Nor does the sun shine there, nor moon, nor fire; to which having gone they return not, that is My supreme abode.

*omityekākṣaraṁ brahma vyāharanmāmanusmaran,*
*yaḥ prayāti tyajandehaṁ sa yāti paramāṁ gatim.* (8.13)

8.13. Uttering the one-syllable Om (the symbol of Brahman) and remembering Me, he who departs, leaving the body, attains the supreme goal.

---

**Questions on Chapter VIII**

1. What are the six vital questions asked by Arjuna with which the chapter begins? (1-2)
2. What was the explanation of antaḥkāla and what is meant by prayāṇakāla? (5)
3. What is rebirth? (6)
4. How does an individual get his rebirth? (6-8)
5. What are the tips given by Lord Kṛṣṇa to develop a constant Īśvara smaraṇa? (9-13)
6. What are the adjustments necessary for the practice of concentrated meditations upon the supreme goal? (14-15)
7. Kṛṣṇa declares that 'everything in the world including brahmaloka changes but I am the One who is the substratum of all beings and he who attains Me never gets any rebirth!, Is the blue boy of Vrindavan so powerful? (16)

8. What is the higher path of 'non-return' and what is the lower path of returning again? (23-26)

9. What is pravṛitti mārga and what exactly is the opposite of it? (23-26)

10. What is meant by the path of light and the path of darkness? (23-26)

# Chapter IX

## Rājavidyā-rajaguhya-yoga

(Yoga of Royal Knowledge & Royal Secret)

[The release from worldly bondage can be obtained by considering one's work as an act of worship of the Lord, offered with the right knowledge that He is everywhere and in everything, and yet, He is, at the same time, distinct from it all always. The path of Knowledge and the path of ignorance.]

Lord Kṛṣṇa: "I shall now impart to you, Arjuna, the essential secret of the greatest Knowledge, as you are very attentive and eager to know more. The theoretical knowledge of Truth and the technique of its application, the path of knowledge will make you fit for the realisation of 'Me in you'. The implication of this spiritual science is profound, and it is the greatest subjective knowledge one can ever possess about oneself. One can put this entirely into practice and gain self-perfection, become the Self. On the contrary, those who do not have faith and conviction in the truth of this Knowledge and therefore, do not undertake the pilgrimage to the Self, fritter away their physical strength, mental powers and intellectual capacities, running after material pleasures on the path of ignorance. The result for them is the unending rounds of birth and death. They wander farther and farther away from the shrine of the Self.

> [Where can one come to recognise and experience the unmanifest Self, the immutable Reality which is the Self in every being?]

I told you, Arjuna, that I am subtler than the subtlest. In philosophy the subtlety of a thing is measured by its pervasiveness. Since I am subtler than the subtlest, I am, indeed all-pervasive. There is nothing in the universe, which is not pervaded by Me. But I do not identify Myself with anything, with the joys and sorrows or with the other changes and conditionings.

If you ponder deeply over this fact, you will understand that I do not have any sort of attachment to the finite manifested universe. This indifference, this dispassion I can keep due to My yoga-śakti.

The finite universe with its multiplicity of forms is as false and as unreal as a dream. Only one, who is 'awake' in the spiritual sense of the term, can fully cognise the oneness of the Self. To such a fully enlightened one, there is no finite unreal universe. It does not exist at all. So this relationship that seems to exist between the infinite Self and the finite universe is due to my divine power only".

Arjuna: What is the lot of the beings, who to the gross intellect seem to exist and are said to be created by the Creator at the dawn of his day and dissolved at the approach of his night?

> [No Creator apart from the Lord. He is the only cause for everything. Everything comes from Him, exists in Him and in the end dissolves into Him.]

Lord Kṛṣṇa: "These beings, strictly speaking, are neither created by a Creator different from Me nor destroyed by a destroyer other than Me. The creation, the dissolution, the unending cycle of births and deaths, are all My play only.

But this play is itself not in fact played by Me, as I am indifferent and untouched by it. So no vāsanā is left behind upon Me. My play itself is but an apparent experience".

Arjuna: "Prakṛti – Lord's lower nature I accept it, but I cannot understand it. Please explain a little further what this lower nature is".

Lord Kṛṣṇa: "Prakṛti – My lower nature – is powerless by itself. But I, the Puruṣa, the eternal Self, lend my power to her and then from her is produced the world of living beings and inert objects. I preside over this process, but do not take any active part at all in it. I remain as pure and as untainted after the work as I was ever before it. I am immaculate always.

When I explained to you about my lower and higher nature, I told you that men of imperfect knowledge get confused between the manifested Me and the unmanifested Me. I come down in my form at My free will to bless the generation, but that form is only produced by My māyā.[1] Therefore, that form should not be mistaken for the real Me.

Entertaining meaningless hopes, performing useless actions, and possessing imperfect knowledge, the ignorant men get nowhere near Me. While the wise, knowing the common underlying principle in everything to be the Lord, worship Me with matchless devotion. Certainly they do come to Me in their full evolutionary maturity.

> [Worship of the Lord: What constitutes a truly worshipping heart? What is His nature that I must invoke for the purposes of His worship? Is He one? Is He distinct from all other things? Is He many? In my worship of Him what should I ask of Him? Will the devotee discover all fulfilment at His feet?]

---

[1] यदा यदा हि धर्मस्य ग्लानिर्भवति भारत ।
अभ्युत्थानमधर्मस्य तदात्मानं सृजाम्यहम् ॥ ४·७ ॥
*yadā yadā hi dharmasya glānirbhavati bhārata,*
*abhyutthānamadharmasya tadātmānaṁ sṛjāmyaham.* (4.7)

4.7 Whenever there is decay of righteousness, O Bhārata, and rise of unrighteousness, then I manifest Myself.

परित्राणाय साधूनां विनाशाय च दुष्कृताम् ।
धर्मसंस्थापनार्थाय सम्भवामि युगे युगे ॥ ४·८ ॥
*paritrāṇāya sādhūnāṁ vināśāya ca duṣkṛtām,*
*dharmasaṁsthāpanārthāya sambhavāmi yuge yuge.* (4.8)

4.8 For the protection of the good, for the destruction of the wicked and for the establishment of righteousness, I am born in every age.

The good and wise men sing My glories, silently and incessantly, all through their activities and expressions in life. Resisting temptations courageously, they live an austere and disciplined life, always rejecting the wrong and ever accepting only that which is the right. They love Me so well that they surrender completely to my Will at their physical, mental and intellectual levels, to the utter annihilation of their personal ego-sense.

There are those who see Me at once as (1) the One, (2) The One, yet as distinct, and (3) as the manifold. They see Me as the one sole subtle essential Principle, underlying in all, but they also realise that I am distinct from them all, and though One, I appear to be many. Through all their experiences in life, they alone keep constant company with Me.

I appear as many to the gross intellect. I am the sacrifice and the sacrificial materials. I am the fire in which the oblations are offered. I am the mantra, the sacred hymn, with which the divine is invoked. In short, there is nothing other than Me.

I am the loving grandfather, the father and the mother of the universe. I am also the Vedas, the Ṛg, the Sāma and the Yajur'. I am the sacred symbol 'Om', which indicates the highest state of pure Awareness, the fourth state of Consciousness (turīya), along with the three ordinary states of Consciousness – the waking (jāgrata), the dream (svapna) and the deep sleep (suṣupti). I am the One, who dispenses rewards for all actions of all creatures. I am the pure One that is to be known.

I am the ultimate destination. All come to Me ultimately. I am the ruler and the witness of all, refuge of the distressed and the friend of the lonely. I am the origin as well as the end; the foundations and the support, the changeless seed, from which the finite world sprang into existence, as also the treasure house of things.

I give heat. I send forth or withhold rain. I am immortality, as well as death. I am existence and also non-existence. Thus, nothing is there which I am not.

There are the Vaidika scholars, who worship Me by performing sacrifices as prescribed in the Vedas, and ask for the pleasures of heaven. I fulfil their desires. They enjoy the divine pleasures in the heavens for a time, according to their merit and when the merit gets exhausted by enjoyment, they are born again in the mortal world. These elaborate sacrificial rituals, because they are motivated by the desire to enjoy the ethical pleasures, fail to bring about the final release from the bondage of wordly existence.

But those who worship Me, meditating constantly and steadily upon Me, to the exclusion of all other thoughts, come to Me. For them, there is no fear of rebirth and worldly sufferings. I help them. I guard them always.

Even those who worship other deities worship Me only, but in an indirect way, for, I am the ultimate recipient of all the offerings, offered to other gods. But since they do not recognise Me as the one God above all other gods, they are born again and again in this world.

> [Some important points on worship: In order to make our worship of the Lord efficient to the maximum and fully beneficial to us, let us have some instructions, please.]

Arjuna, I must warn you here. You should not think that very costly materials or elaborate rites as prescribed in the Vedas are required for my worship. What you offer is insignificant. I do not even look at what is offered to me. The most important part is with what intention, purity of motive, you offer it to Me. Fruit or flower, leaf or water can be the symbols of your intention. But when offered with faith and in the right attitude, I accept it all with great pleasure.[1]

[1] LEAF: During her stay in the forest, Draupadī could offer only a bit of a cooked leaf, sticking to her akṣayapātra to Kṛṣṇa, when He came to save her from Durvāsa's curse. It was offered with such reverence and tenderness of heart that it appeased His hunger. Durvāsa and his ten thousand disciples, who came begging for food, at the advice of Duryodhana to disgrace the Pāṇḍavas, went away with a feeling of having eaten too much, without touching a morsel of food.

FLOWER: In the Gajendramokṣa story, Indradyumna, the Pāṇḍya king was cursed to become an elephant by sage Agastya. He became an elephant but was caught, when sporting in a river, by a crocodile. In the struggle between the elephant and the crocodile, the former offered a lotus flower, freshly plucked in a flash of devotion. He was released immediately not only from the temporary distress and curse but from worldly bondage itself.

FRUIT: The story of Śabarī, tasting to find the sweetest fruit to be offered to the Lord, and her offering of the half eaten ones, and the Lord receiving it with extreme happiness is an unforgettable example.

WATER: Water is an essential material, always offered in all modes of worship.

Besides all these, the story of Kuchela offering the low quality beaten-rice is too well known to need any repetition here.

In all the illustrations given, the materials offered are apparently worthless and cheap but became priceless treasures in His eyes because He saw only the intense faith and devotion behind them.

Therefore, consider your work as worship and your food as an oblation to Me. Offer gifts in My name. Practise penance for Me. Nay, whatever you do, consider it as an offering unto Me. Remember Me, constantly, all through your activities.

When you thus consider Me as the agent of all your activities, you are freed from the vāsanā-bondage caused by them.

[Sannyāsa and yoga – Lord's attitude to all sinnners reformed into saints.]

Thus by sannyāsa (renunciation of all egocentric activities) and by yoga (non-attachment to the anxieties for their fruits), meaning constant remembrance of the Lord, which is but a natural sequence of sannyāsa, you will reach Me.

I am partial to none. I hate none. I love none. But those who worship Me constantly remembering Me, come to reside in Me. Therefore, I too, come to reside in them.

I invariably forget and forgive the past sins of one, who resolves to tread the path of the good. His intention being noble, he is to be complimented upon his resolve to reform himself. He shall, from then on, pursue the good path with determination, because he has embraced that path with faith and conviction. I will see that he attains immense peace.

My devotee, be he a vaiśya or a śūdra, a man or a woman, shall never come to suffer.

When even sinners can attain salvation by constantly remembering Me, why not the virtuous and the moral man? So Arjuna, always remember Me. Ever remain My devotee. Sacrifice to Me. Identify yourself with Me. You will know nothing but peace and joy in life".

---

अनन्याश्चिन्तयन्तो मां ये जनाः पर्युपासते ।
तेषां नित्याभियुक्तानां योगक्षेमं वहाम्यहम् ॥ ९·२२ ॥

*ananyāścintayanto māṁ ye janāḥ paryupāsate,*
*teṣāṁ nityābhiyuktānāṁ yogakṣemaṁ vahāmyaham.* (9.22)

9.22 To those men who worship Me alone, thinking of no other, to those ever self-controlled, I secure which is not already possessed (yoga) and preserve what they already possess (kṣema).

पत्रं पुष्पं फलं तोयं यो मे भक्त्या प्रयच्छति ।
तदहं भक्त्युपहृतमश्नामि प्रयतात्मनः ॥ ९·२६ ॥

*patraṁ puṣpaṁ phalaṁ toyam yo me bhaktyā prayacchati,*
*tadahaṁ bhaktyupahṛtamaśnāmi prayatātmanaḥ.* (9.26)

9.26 Whoever offers Me with devotion a leaf, a flower, a fruit, water, that offered by the pure minded with devotion, I accept.

---

## Questions on Chapter IX

1. What do we mean by rahasya? (1)
2. What is the truth behind the world we perceive? (4)
3. What are the six points with which Lord Kṛṣṇa establishes his relationship with the world? (5-6)
4. Lord Kṛṣṇa says that 'I create the world with the help of prakṛti. I am not contaminated by the happiness or misery of the world'. Is it right for the Lord to create the world and give sorrow and misery for the world, and enjoy Himself without any obstacle? (7-9)
5. Enumerate the different kinds of worship. (11-15)
6. What is the difference between āsurī prakṛti and daivī prakṛti? (12-13)

7. Lord says, "I created the world, I am the homa, yoga, mantra, the ghee used for the homa," and so on. In that he says, "I am the mother, I am the father" and so on. If father and mother are one and the same how could the creation have taken place and where could it be, if everything is but that One truth only? (16-19)

8. What does the soma-juice drink denote? Is there any shrub like that whose juice can intoxicate a man? (20)

9. What is the difference between those who worship for the sake of desire fulfilment and those who worship for the very love of Lord Himself? (21-25)

10. What are the essential things which must be present when one does offerings to Lord Kṛṣṇa? (26-27)

11. In stanza 29, it is said that I have no hatred or love towards any of the beings. But the second half of the stanza says that those who worship Me with devotion, they are in Me and I am also in them. Explain this paradoxical statement. (29)

12. Quote that stanza which states that even the worst sort of sinner can evolve into a good natured one if only he desires to do. (30)

13. Are the women, vaiśyas and śūdras so low that Lord considers them as exceptional cases? (32)

14. When Lord Kṛṣṇa says that you will attain Me what does it mean? How does this excel more than the joys of svarga? (33-34)

# Chapter X

## Vibhūti-yoga

(Yoga of Divine Glories)

[The glories of the Lord – The Lord of the universe – Compare this title with that of the following chapter – A brief and approximate analysis of the perceptible glories of the Lord as can be understood by the common intellect is given here.]

The indweller (jīvātmā) of all beings is the supreme Self (Paramātmā). Whatever is glorious, auspicious or prominent in anything, that is a shadow, a sign of His splendour only. He is the Supreme and the essential Factor, common in all objects and beings, without which no specimen of any species can remain as they do. The Lord enlightens Arjuna on how best he can keep in touch with this eternal aspect of the Truth even when he is perceiving the pluralistic world.]

Lord Kṛṣṇa : "Arjuna, even the gods and the great sages do not correctly understand My greatness, though I am their cause. I am birthless and beginningless. I am the sole Lord of the universe. Any mortal who knows this truth sheds all his sins.

Intellect, wisdom, non-delusion, forgiveness, truth, self-restraint, tranquility, joy, sorrow, birth, death, fearlessness, non-injury, equanimity, contentment, penance, generosity, fame, ill-fame, all these, which are experienced by beings, spring from Me alone.

The four manus, the progenitors of the human race, and the seven great sages[1] are created by My willpower. One who knows this great glory of Mine is a true yogī.

The wise, joyfully and with intense eagerness worship Me, knowing Me to be the sources of all. They know that everything evolves from Me alone. Entertaining the one idea that I am everything, diverting all their energies towards Me, they sing my glories. They take delight in talking about Me. Yes, they revel in Me. The Bliss realised by living in and for the Lord has no comparison whatsoever with even the greatest joy promised by the world or imagined by the human mind. I bless such wise men with buddhi-yoga – a deeply penetrating and pure intellectual faculty

[1] Marīci, Aṅgirasa, Atri, Pulaha, Pulastya, Kṛtu and Vasiṣtha.

to comprehend through meditation the real nature of the Self. This luminous lamp of wisdom dispels all the darkness of ignorance in them. The Self – the Lord within – shines out for them in all its glory".

Arjuna : "My Lord, Nārada, Vyāsa and other great seers of old have described You in the same terms. Now, You too, confirm their teachings, I believe fully that You are the supreme Spirit – the Lord – the infinite Paramātman.

You told me earlier that even the gods and the great sages do not correctly comprehend You in all your glory. So, there is no use asking them to teach me the Truth about You. Since You are the only one who knows You, You are the only teacher, who can teach me about Yourself and Your glories, You must tell me, therefore, all Your glories, which pervade all the worlds.

Tell me also, how am I to meditate so that I may come to know You. In which aspect or form should I contemplate upon You to realise You in Your full glory? Tell me all about Your yoga-powers and Your glories".

Lord Kṛṣṇa : "Yes. Since there is no end to the list of My glories, I can only indicate to you but some of the most prominent ones among them all.

Briefly, I am the divine life spark in all beings, I am the Creator, the Protector and the Destroyer of all beings.[1]

[1] The Lord indicates His presence in varieties of objects, He is the essential Principle, running through all these objects, without which the object ceases to exist as that object.

रसोऽहमप्सु कौन्तेय प्रभास्मि शशिसूर्ययोः ।
प्रणवः सर्ववेदेषु शब्दः खे पौरुषं नृषु ॥ ७.८ ॥

*raso'hamapsu kaunteya prabhāsmi śaśisūryayoḥ,*
*praṇavaḥ sarvavedeṣu śabdaḥ khe pauruṣaṁ nṛṣu.* (7.8)

7.8. I am the sapidity in water, O son of Kuntī, I am the light in the moon and the sun; I am the syllable Om in all the Vedas, sound in ether, and virility in men.

पुण्यो गन्धः पृथिव्यां च तेजश्चास्मि विभावसौ ।
जीवनं सर्वभूतेषु तपश्चास्मि तपस्विषु ॥ ७.९ ॥

*puṇyo gandhaḥ pṛthivyāṁ ca tejaścāsmi vibhāvasau,*
*jīvanaṁ sarvabhuteṣu tapaścāsmi tapasviṣu.* (7.9)

7.9. I am the sweet fragrance in earth and the brilliance in the fire, the life in all beings, and I am austerity in the austere.

बीजं मां सर्वभूतानां विद्धि पार्थ सनातनम् ।
बुद्धिर्बुद्धिमतामस्मि तेजस्तेजस्विनामहम् ॥ ७.१० ॥

*bījaṁ maṁ sarvabhūtānāṁ viddhi pārtha sanātanam,*
*buddhirbuddhimatāmasmi tejastejasvināmaham.* (7.10)

7.10. Know Me, O Pārtha, as the eternal seed of all beings; I am the intelligence of the intelligent; the splendour of the splendid (things and beings), am I.

बलं बलवतां चाहं कामरागविवर्जितम् ।
धर्माविरुद्धो भूतेषु कामोऽस्मि भरतर्षभ ॥ ७.११ ॥

*balaṁ balavatāṁ cāhaṁ kāmarāgavivarjitam,*
*dharmāviruddho bhūteṣu kāmo'smi bharatarṣabha.* (7.11)

7.11. Of the strong, I am the strength – devoid of desire and attachment, and in (all) beings, I am the desire – unopposed to dharma, O best among the Bharatas.

I am Viṣṇu among the 12 ādityas; the sun among the luminaries; Marīci among the maruts; the moon among the stars; *Sāma-veda* among the three Vedas; Indra among the Gods; mind among the senses; intellect of the living beings; Śaṅkara among the rudras; Kubera among the semi-divine and evil spirits; Agni among the eight vasus; Meru among the mountains; Bṛhaspati among the priests; Skanda[1] among the army generals; the ocean among the reservoirs of waters; Bhṛgu among the great sages; the sacred syllable Om among words, japa-yajña[2] among sacrifices; Himalayas among the immovables; Pipala-tree among the trees; Nārada among the celestial sages; Citraratha among the gandharvas; Kapila among the seers; Uccaiḥśravā among the horses; Airāvata among the elephants; the king among men; Vajra[3] among the weapons; Kāmadhenu[4] among cows; Madana, the God of love, the cause of birth; Vāsuki among serpents; Ananta among the snakes; Varūṇa among the water deities; Aryamā – the king of the dead forefathers among the pitṛs; Yama, the God of death, among the controllers; Prahlāda among the daityas; Time among

1 Kārtikeya, son of Lord Śiva.

2 Silent repetition of the Lord's name.

3 The thunder-bolt of Indra.

4 The Divine wish-yielding cow.

the instruments of measurement; lion among the beasts; Garūḍa among birds; wind among the purifiers; Śrī Rāma among the heroes; Shark among the fishes; the Ganga among the rivers; the beginning, the middle and the end of all created things; the science of the Self among all the sciences; the faculty of speaking in the orators; the vowel 'A' of the alphabets; dvandva compound among compounds[1].

I am the everlasting time, the dispenser of all fruits of actions. I am the all-devouring death of the created beings and the source of all those who are yet to be created.

I am also fame, prosperity, speech, memory, intelligence; firmness and forgiveness among the feminine qualities.

I am the Bṛhatsāma[2] among the sacred hymns; Gāyatrī among metres; Mārgaśīrṣa-month[3] among the twelve months; and Vasanta, the spring season, among the six seasons.

---

[1] Compound words: samasta-padas, dvandva-samāsa is a specific kind of word conjunction.

[2] The Vaidika hymns composed in bṛhati metre.

[3] December 15$^{th}$ to January 15$^{th}$.

I am, moreover, the gambling of the deceitful; splendour of the splendid or the excellence of the excellent; victory of the victorious; perseverance of the persevering; the goodness in the good.

I am Kṛṣṇa among the Yādavas; Arjuna among the Pāṇḍavas; Vyāsa among the recluses; Śukra among the wisest; royal sceptre among the chastisers; statescraft of those desiring vicory; silence of secrets; and the Knowledge of the knowing ones.

In short, I am the changeless seed of all. Neither the movables nor the immovables can ever exist without Me.

Remember, Arjuna, what I have given you is not an exhaustive list of my marvellous glories but only a brief indication of a few of them. Whatever that is marvellous, excellent, prosperous or prominent in any being or object, understand that to be an expression of a part of My glory.

Is there any need for more details? You know enough when you know that the entire universe is supported by a part of My own Self".

## Questions on Chapter X

1. In the $10^{th}$ chapter the Lord says that 'one must know Me as unborn beginningless'. We come to know things only through our mind. Mind perceives only those things which have beginning, growth and end.Therefore, how is it possible to 'know' that which has no beginning and end? (3)

2. How did creation take place according to *Gītā*? (6)

3. What is microcosm and macrocosm? (7)

4. To whom does the Lord give buddhi-yoga? (9-11)

5. How does Arjuna praise Lord Śrī Kṛṣṇa? (12-15)

6. After praising Lord Kṛṣṇa, what did he want to 'know'? (16-18)

7. Describe 'meditation upon the Lord', as explained by the Gītācārya. (20-42)

# Chapter XI

## Viśvarūpa-darśana-yoga

(Yoga of Vision of the Divine Cosmic Form)

[Viśvarūpa darśana – the universe in the Lord. Note the contrast of this title with that of the previous chapter.]

The universe of endless forms is pervaded by Paramātman and yet it is invisible to the ordinary eyes and incomprehensible to the ordinary intellect. This can be observed or inwardly experienced with the 'eyes' of faith and knowledge.

Arjuna blessed by Kṛṣṇa with the 'subtle divine eyes' (divya-cakṣus) was shown the real form (viśvarūpa) of Śrī Kṛṣṇa Paramātman, serving as the very substratum for the entire universe.]

Arjuna: "I am deeply grateful to you, my Lord, for teaching me the secret science of the Self. My ignorance has left me. I understand that you are the only Master, who commands creation and dissolution. I comprehend also your endless glories.

Now, I beg of You, my Lord, that if you consider me to be fit to see Your real divine form, bless me by showing it".

Lord Kṛṣṇa: "I am quite pleased with your devotion and understanding. So, I shall show you My viśvarūpa, wherein you will see the twelve ādityas, eleven rudras, two aśvini devas, seven maruts and many other divine forms of different shapes and colours, as also many other marvels. Nay, you can see the entire universe of movables and immovables in Me. You may also see whatever else you wish to see.

What I am going to show is My form infinite. With your two physical eyes, it is impossible to see that divine form, so, I shall give you the subtle divine vision (divya -cakṣus)".

Lord Kṛṣṇa then showed Arjuna His viśvarūpa, which embraces the heavens, the earth and the other world. Arjuna was struck with wonder mingled with awe at the wonderful resplendent sight. He prostrated before the Lord in great reverence and with folded palms addressed Him thus:

Arjuna: "My Lord, I see in You, the heaven with Brahmā, seated on a lotus, Śivā and other gods, the mortal world of living beings and sages and the world of serpents.[1]

I see your endless form Itself, without a beginning, a middle and an end. How many arms, stomachs, mouths and eyes You have! I can see You as Viṣṇu, with the crown, mace and discus. You are pure lustre Itself, as replendent as the blazing sun and fire, spreading lustre all round.[2]

---

[1] अर्जुन उवाच

*Arjuna uvāca*

पश्यामि देवांस्तव देव देहे सर्वांस्तथा भूतविशेषसङ्घान् ।
ब्रह्माणमीशं कमलासनस्थमृषींश्च सर्वानुरगांश्च दिव्यान् ॥ ११·१५ ॥

*paśyāmi devāṁstava deva dehe sarvāṁstathā bhūtaviśeṣasaṅghān,*
*brahmāṇamīśaṁ kamalāsanastham-ṛṣīṁśca sarvānuragāṁśca*
*divyān.* (11.15)

11.15 Arjuna said : I see all the gods, O God, in Your body, and (also) hosts of various classes of beings, Brahmā, the lord of creation, seated on the lotus, all the ṛṣis and celestial serpents.

[2] अनेकबाहूदरवक्त्रनेत्रं पश्यामि त्वां सर्वतोऽनन्तरूपम् ।
नान्तं न मध्यं न पुनस्तवादिं पश्यामि विश्वेश्वर विश्वरूप ॥ ११·१६ ॥

*anekabāhūdaravaktranetraṁ paśyāmi tvāṁ sarvato'nantarūpam,*
*nāntaṁ na madhyaṁ na punastavādiṁ paśyāmi viśveśvara*
*viśvarūpa.* (11.16)

11.16 I see Thee of boundless form on every side with manifold arms, stomachs, mouths and eyes; neither the end, nor the middle, nor also the beginning, and so on, I see, O! Lord of the universe!

Indeed, You are the one supreme Lord, the Almighty, worthy to be known and to be sought. You are the only changeless substratum of the three worlds. You are the permanent guardian of the eternal dharma. You are the most ancient Puruṣa.

The sun and the moon are Your eyes; burning fire Your mouth. The whole universe seems to me to be one mass of lustre. You have assumed a frightening form, pervading the entire space that all the three worlds seem to be trembling.[1]

[1] किरीटिनं गदिनं चक्रिणं च तेजोराशिं सर्वतो दीप्तिमन्तम् ।
पश्यामि त्वां दुर्निरीक्ष्यं समन्ताद्दीप्तानलार्कद्युतिमप्रमेयम् ॥ ११·१७ ॥
*kirīṭinaṁ gadinaṁ cakriṇaṁ ca tejorāśiṁ sarvato dīptimantam,*
*paśyāmi tvāṁ durnirīkṣyaṁ samantāddīptānalārkadyutimaprameyam.* (11.17)

11.17. I see Thee with crown, club and discus; a mass of radiance shining everywhere, very hard to look at, all round blazing like burning fire and sun, and incomprehensible.

त्वमक्षरं परमं वेदितव्यं त्वमस्य विश्वस्य परं निधानम् ।
त्वमव्ययः शाश्वतधर्मगोप्ता सनातनस्त्वं पुरुषो मतो मे ॥ ११·१८ ॥
*tvamakṣaraṁ paramaṁ veditavyaṁ tvamasya viśvasya paraṁ nidhānam,*
*tvamavyayaḥ śāśvatadharmagoptā sanātanastavaṁ puruṣo mato me.* (11.18)

11.18 Thou art the Imperishable, the supreme Being worthy to be known. Thou art the great treasure house of this universe; Thou art the imperishable Protector of the eternal dharma. In my opinion, Thou art the ancient Puruṣa.

अनादिमध्यान्तमनन्तवीर्यमनन्तबाहुं शशिसूर्यनेत्रम् ।
पश्यामि त्वां दीप्तहुताशवक्त्रं स्वतेजसा विश्वमिदं तपन्तम् ॥ ११·१९ ॥

Contd.......

I can see various scenes. In one place the gods and in another the sages and the seers in a group praising You, with joined palms. I see also the ādityas, the rudras, the vasus, the aśvinis, the maruts, the pitṛs, the gandharvas, the yakṣas, the asuras, many others standing stunned, looking at You in awe and trembling with terror.

Your infinite form, beginning and ending nowhere, embracing the entire universe is surely frightening. Be gracious, My Lord.

My Lord, as you promised that you would show me whatever else I wish to see, I see now

---

Contd.......

*anādimadhyāntamanantavīryamanantabāhuṁ śaśisūryanetram,*
*paśyāmi tvāṁ dīptahutāśavaktraṁ svatejasā viśvamidaṁ tapantam.* (11.19)

11.19 I see You without beginning, middle or end, infinite in power, of endless arms, the sun and the moon being Your eyes, the burning fire Your mouth heating the whole universe with Your radiance.

द्यावापृथिव्योरिदमन्तरं हि व्याप्तं त्वयैकेन दिशश्च सर्वाः ।
दृष्ट्वाद्भुतं रुपमुग्रं तवेदं लोकत्रयं प्रव्यथितं महात्मन् ॥ ११·२० ॥

*dyāvāpṛthivyoridamantaraṁ hi vyāptaṁ tvayaikena diśaśca sarvāḥ,*
*dṛṣṭvādbhutaṁ rūpamugraṁ tavedaṁ lokatrayaṁ pravyathitaṁ mahātman.* (11.20)

11.20 This space between the earth and the heaven and all the quarters are filled by You alone; having seen this Your wonderful and terrible form, the three worlds are trembling with fear, O great-souled Being.

the very same battlefield of Kurukṣetra, where the Kauravas with their allies, as also Bhīṣma, Droṇa and Karṇa rush forward to Your terrific mouth and disappear. The great heroes on our side too, follow them into Your crushing jaws. This grand moving procession of heroes on both sides to Your mouth is exactly like the flow of the rivers towards the sea. Just as the moths hurriedly rush into the blazing fire and get destroyed themselves, so too all these heroes run to Your mouth for their death. Oh! my God! You have swallowed the entire universe, still you do not seem to be satiated.

Your fierce rays fill up the entire space. There is nothing but effulgence everywhere.

I cannot comprehend the meaning of this magnificent vision. Be pleased to tell me who You are, so fierce in form. My humble homage to You, the Lord Supreme. Tell me Your purpose in showing me this fierce form".

Lord Kṛṣṇa: "You have seen just now My aspect as destroyer of the universe. You think that you would be bringing destruction to your enemies, if you take part in the battle. No. You do not. Even without you, the entire hosts of the wicked, ranged on the other side, will die.

Therefore, my friend, get up and conquer your enemies. They are already slain by Me. You are a mere instrument. You can enjoy the fame and the unrivalled kingdom even now. Why do you hesitate to discharge your arrows at your teacher, your grandfather, your kinsmen, and your friends? Are you still afraid that you would be their destroyer? I am their destroyer and not you. Therefore, be not grieved. Take courage and fight".

Hearing these encouraging words Arjuna shed his fear a little and praised the Lord thus:

Arjuna: "It is but fitting that the world of the good should rejoice in singing Your praises and the world of the wicked run away in panic. There is nothing strange in the good praising You. Because You are greater than the greatest and the Creator of even the Creator Brahmā. You are the Imperishable, the Manifest and the Unmanifest. You are the most Ancient; the sole supreme Lord. You are the Knower and the Knowable. You are the only Abode of the entire universe. You appear in infinite forms. You are Vāyu, Yama, Agni, Varūṇa, Moon, Prajāpati and all the gods rolled into one. I am unable to describe You. My humble prostrations again and again to You.

Pardon me, O! Lord, for whatever I have said, not knowing Your greatness, calling You familiarly and intimately as 'Kṛṣṇa' and 'my friend'. I confess I have committed many wrongs, by teasing You, by making fun of You, while at play or resting, sitting or at meals. I beg of You humbly to pardon all my sins.

You are the Father of three worlds. You are the Almighty to be adored by everyone. You are the greatest Teacher. There is none equal to You in all the three worlds. How can there be one superior to You! Your greatness is inconceivable!

Be pleased to accept my humble homage, I crave Your forgiveness. Just as a father forgives his son, a friend his friend, a lover his beloved, so also You should forgive me and bless me!

I am extremely delighted to see Your universal form, which was never before seen by anyone. But my mind is slightly disturbed by fear too. So be pleased to resume Your previous beautiful form with Your usual four arms, O! Lord, with the crown, the mace and the discus!"

Lord Kṛṣṇa : "I have shown you by My yogic power My viśvarūpa – an aspect of Me as the destroyer, which is not yet seen by anyone. It is impossible to be seen even by a deep study of the scriptures, elaborate sacrifices, munificent gifts or severe penance. Do not be terrified at its sight. See now My mild human vaiśṇava form".

Assuming again the smiling vaiśṇava form, Kṛṣṇa continues.

Lord Kṛṣṇa: "It is extremely hard to see My Viśvarūpa. Don't forget that even the gods long for nothing else. I repeat that none can see this form by any of the known sādhanās – study of scriptures, sacrifices, gifts or penance. Single minded devotion to Me alone will help one to see Me, to know Me, and to ultimately reach Me.

Those who are free from attachment and hatred and who dedicate all their actions to Me with unswerving faith, knowing Me to be the supreme Lord come to me. This is sure and ever guaranteed".

---

## Questions on Chapter XI

1. After knowing the glory of the Lord, what did Arjuna want to perceive? (2-4)
2. What was the answer given by Lord Kṛṣṇa? (5-8)
3. When Sañjaya said that the Lord showed his viśvarūpa, what does it signify? (9-13)
4. What did Arjuna perceive? (15)
5. What is the meaning when Lord Kṛṣṇa says "I have slain those people already. You act only as an instrument"? (33-34)
6. What was the change in Arjuna's personality after the viśvarūpa darśana? (51)
7. Who can afford to see the Lord's supreme form? (48,54-55)

# Chapter XII

## Bhakti-yoga

(Yoga of Devotion)

[Bhakti-yoga – The science of devotion to the Lord – Devotion is the devotee's identification with the Lord of his heart. To meditate upon the unmanifest formless God is very difficult, even though that is the superior path. But those who worship the manifest God with intense love by dedicating all their activities to Him get salvation comparatively easily.]

Arjuna: "Which of the two types of devotees – those worshipping You in this form (as manifest in the form of the universe[1]) with firm faith and love, or those worshipping You as the formless and unmanifest – is superior?"

Lord Kṛṣṇa: "Those who have unswerving faith in me, devote undivided attention on Me and practise uninterrupted remembrance of Me are surely

[1] As described in the previous chapter.

better devotees. No doubt, those who worship the unmanifest and indefinable Me with perfect self-control, loving all creatures as they are all My forms, surely do reach Me. But, it is very difficult for one to get completely absorbed in contemplation of the Absolute, to the utter elimination of the ego. So it is advisable for beginners to pursue the former 'path', devotion to the Lord's manifested Form Divine.

[Worship of the manifest God – What must be our attitude towards the Lord of our worship – Four ways of truly worshipping the Lord of our heart with devotion.]

"I am the saviour of those, who dedicate all their activities unto Me, worship Me with pure faith regarding Me as the supreme God. There is no doubt that those who contemplate on Me with undivided attention get salvation.

The first and the best, but the most difficult is to fix the mind on God firmly and keep it there (dhyāna).[1] This may be almost impossible, because

---

[1] मय्येव मन आधत्स्व मयि बुद्धिं निवेशय ।
निवसिष्यसि मय्येव अत ऊर्ध्वं न संशयः ॥ १२·८ ॥

*mayyeva mana ādhatsva mayi buddhiṁ niveśaya,*
*nivasiṣyasi mayyeva ata ūrdhvaṁ na saṁśayaḥ.* (12.8)

12.8 . Fix thy mind on Me only, place thy intellect in Me; then (thereafter) you shall, no doubt, live in Me alone.

the mind wanders away from God. Then by sheer self-effort, bring the mind again and again back to Him (abhyāsa).[1] If constant attempts at repetition (abhyāsa) in concentration also fail, dedicate all the daily activities unto Me,[2] dedicate the 'all -I-do' mentality of your ego unto Me (dhyānam). If this also seems impossible, as you cannot conquer your ego, which is necessary for such a total sense of dedication in all activities, alright, you continue your activities but renounce the 'fruits' thereof unto Me – stop worrying over the 'fruits' (karmaphala-tyāga).[3]

---

[1] अथ चित्तं समाधातुं न शक्नोषि मयि स्थिरम् ।
अभ्यासयोगेन ततो मामिच्छाप्तुं धनञ्जय ॥ १२·९॥
*atha cittaṁ samādhātuṁ na śakanoṣi mayi sthiram,*
*abhyāsayogena tato māmicchāptuṁ dhanañjaya.* (12.9)

12.9 If you are unable to fix your mind steadily on Me, then by the yoga of constant practice you do seek to reach Me, O Dhanañjaya.

[2] अभ्यासेऽप्यसमर्थोऽसि मत्कर्मपरमो भव ।
मदर्थमपि कर्माणि कुर्वन्सिद्धिमवाप्स्यसि ॥ १२·१० ॥
*abhyāse'pyasamartho'si matkarmaparamo bhava,*
*madarthamapi karmāṇi kurvansiddhimavāpsyasi.* (12.10)

12.10 If you are unable even to practise abhyasa-yoga, be you intent on doing actions for My sake; even by doing actions for My sake, you shall attain perfection.

[3] अथैतदप्यशक्तोऽसि कर्तुं मद्योगमाश्रितः ।
सर्वकर्मफलत्यागं ततः कुरु यतात्मवान् ॥ १२-११ ॥
*athaitadapyaśakto'si kartuṁ madyogamāśritaḥ,*
*sarvakarmaphalatyāgaṁ tataḥ kuru yatātmavān.* (12.11)

12.11 If you are unable to do even this then taking refuge in Me, self-controlled, renounce the fruits of all actions.

Knowledge is surely better than practice; meditation is better than knowledge;[1] renunciation

[1] अद्वेष्टा सर्वभूतानां मैत्रः करुण एव च ।
निर्ममो निरहङ्कारः समदुःखसुखः क्षमी ॥ १२-१३ ॥
*adveṣṭā sarvabhūtānāṁ maitraḥ karuṇa eva ca,*
*nirmamo nirahaṅkāraḥ samaduḥkhasukhaḥ kṣamī.* (12.13)

12.13 He who hates no creature, who is friendly and compassionate to all, who is free from attachment and egoism, balanced in pleasure and pain and forgiving.

सन्तुष्टः सततं योगी यतात्मा दृढनिश्चयः ।
मय्यर्पितमनोबुद्धिर्यो मद्भक्तः स मे प्रियः ॥ १२·१४ ॥
*santuṣṭaḥ satataṁ yogī yatātmā dṛḍhaniścayaḥ,*
*mayyarpitamanobuddhiryo madbhaktaḥ sa me priyaḥ.* (12.14)

12.14 Ever content, steady in meditation, self-controlled, possessed of firm conviction with mind and intellect dedicated to Me, he, My devotee, is dear to Me.

यस्मान्नोद्विजते लोको लोकान्नोद्विजते च यः ।
हर्षामर्षभयोद्वेगैर्मुक्तो यः स च मे प्रियः ॥ १२·१५ ॥
*yasmānnodvijate loko lokānnodvijate ca yaḥ,*
*harṣāmarṣabhayodvegairmukto yaḥ sa ca me priyaḥ.* (12.15)

12.15 He by whom the world is not agitated (afflicted), and who cannot be agitated by the world, who is free from joy, envy, fear and anxiety, is dear to Me.

अनपेक्षः शुचिर्दक्ष उदासीनो गतव्यथः ।
सर्वारम्भपरित्यागी यो मद्भक्तः स मे प्रियः ॥ १२·१६ ॥
*anapekṣaḥ śucirdakṣa udāsīno gatavyathaḥ,*
*sarvārambhaparityāgī yo madbhaktaḥ sa me priyaḥ.* (12.16)

12.16 He who is free from wants, pure, alert, unconcerned, untroubled, renouncing all undertakings (or commencements) he who is (thus) devoted to Me, is dear to Me.

Contd......

of the fruits of action is still better than meditation because peace immediately follows such a renunciation of your clinging expectations for reward.

[The Mental attitude of those worshipping the unmanifest Lord – How best can meditation be nourished?]

These are the main characteristics of all My sincere devotees:

(1) hating none

(2) loving and kind to all

(3) free from attachment and the sense of 'mine'

---

Contd......

यो न हृष्यति न द्वेष्टि न शोचति न काङ्क्षति ।
शुभाशुभपरित्यागी भक्तिमान्यः स मे प्रियः ॥ १२·१७ ॥

*yo na hṛṣyati na dveṣṭi na śocati na kāṅkṣati,*
*śubhāśubhaparityāgī bhaktimānyaḥ sa me priyaḥ.* (12.17)

12.17 He who neither rejoices nor hates, nor grieves nor desires, renouncing good and evil, full of devotion, is dear to Me.

समः शत्रौ च मित्रे च तथा मानापमानयोः ।
शीतोष्णसुखदुःखेषु समः सङ्गविवर्जितः ॥ १२-१८ ॥

*samaḥ śatrau ca mitre ca tathā mānāpamānayoḥ,*
*śītoṣṇasukhaduḥkheṣu samaḥ saṅgavivarjitaḥ.* (12.18)

12.18 He who is the same to foe and friend, and also in honour and dishonour, who is the same in cold and heat and in pleasure and pain, who is free from attachment.

(4) undisturbed in pain and pleasure

(5) forgiving

(6) always content

(7) constant in contemplation

(8) ever self-controlled

(9) of firm resolve

(10) with mind and intellect firmly fixed on Me

(11) not disturbing others

(12) not disturbed by others

(13) not jumping about in ecstasy in wordly joys

(14) absolutely free from feelings of envy, fear and anxiety

(15) not depending on the external world for one's own peace of mind

(16) physically clean and mentally pure

(17) efficient

(18) free from desires and worries

(19) not arrogating to oneself the credit for actions

(20) not putting any value on material gains and material losses, as the world is unreal and perishable

(21) loving equally those who injure and those who help

(22) unaffected by honour and dishonour, remaining the same in joy and grief, heat and cold as these are only passing phases

(23) looking at praise and censure with a detached mind

(24) mostly silent

(25) content with whatever is available; and

(26) not having any shelter other than Me.

Such devotees are indeed very very dear to Me. When they have these qualities they need not seek Me; for I shall be running after them – I love them so much indeed".

---

**Questions on Chapter XII**

1. State and explain the most popular question on religion, which Arjuna put to Lord Kṛṣṇa. (1)
2. Why does the Lord say that the bhaktas are the best? Is there any particular reason? (2)
3. Why it is said that nirguṇopāsanā is more difficult than saguṇopāsanā? (5)

4. What are the four ways of attaching one's self to the Lord? (6-11)

5. What are the qualities enumerated by the Lord, while describing persons who are indeed dear to Him? (13-20)

# Chapter XIII

## Kṣetra-kṣetrajña-vibhāga-yoga

(Yoga of Distinction between Field and Its Knower)

[The prakṛti and the Puruṣa, or the body and the soul are two aspects of the Paramātman. Knowledge about these three (prakṛti, Puruṣa and Paramātman) and of their relationship to each other is the highest Knowledge.]

In this chapter, to make Arjuna understand the theme, Lord Kṛṣṇa has used many terms, all synonyms, to indicate the infinite Lord and His presence among us. The vocabulary employed in this chapter, to indicate the supreme Truth and its higher and lower nature, are listed below:-

**PARAMĀTMAN - BRAHMAN**

| | |
|---|---|
| Parā | aparā |
| Higher Nature | lower nature |
| Kṣetrajña | kṣetra |
| Knower of the Field | the field |
| Puruṣa | prakṛti |

| | |
|---|---|
| Jīvātmā | śarīra |
| The Individual Soul | body |
| Dehi | deha |
| Spirit | matter |

Arjuna : "I wish to learn about prakṛti and Puruṣa and also about kṣetra and Kṣetrajña".

Lord Kṛṣṇa: "The body is called the kṣetra (the field). One who 'knows' this body is called the Kṣetrajña (The Knower of the field). Prakṛti is kṣetra and Puruṣa is Kṣetrajña.

I am the Knower of the field (Kṣetrajña) in all the 'fields' (kṣetra). The greatest knowledge is the knowledge of the real nature of the kṣetra and the Kṣetrajña, and their relationship to Paramātman, the supreme Me".

> [A brief analysis and interpretation of the field (kṣetra) and the Knower of the field (Kṣetrajña), what is the body (kṣetra) and who knows all the experiences of the body, the experiencer in me (Kṣetrajña).]

Arjuna: "What is the nature of the kṣetra? What are its modifications? Who is Kṣetrajña? What are His powers?"

Lord Kṛṣṇa: "Direct, convincing and conclusive answers to all these questions are given exhaustively in the Vedas by the great seers[1] when they discuss directly the nature of the Brahman, the supreme Reality.

The Kṣetra, familiarly known as the body, consists of 24 principles (tattvas)[2] with their seven modifications.

---

[1] ऋषिभिर्बहुधा गीतं छन्दोभिर्विविधैः पृथक् ।
ब्रह्मसूत्रपदैश्चैव हेतुमद्भिर्विनिश्चितैः ॥ १३·५ ॥
*ṛṣibhirbahudhā gītaṁ chandobhirvividhaiḥ pṛthak,*
*brahmasūtrapadaiścaiva hetumadbhirviniścitaiḥ.* (13.5)

13.5 Ṛṣis have sung (about the field and the Knower of the field) in many ways, in various distinctive chants and also, in the suggestive words indicative of Brahman, full of reason and decision.

[2] महाभूतान्यहङ्कारो बुद्धिरव्यक्तमेव च ।
इन्द्रियाणि दशैकं च पञ्च चेन्द्रियगोचराः ॥ १३·६ ॥
*mahābhūtānyahaṅkāro buddhiravyaktameva ca,*
*indriyāṇi daśaikaṁ ca pañca cendriyagocarāḥ.* (13.6)

13.6 The great elements, egoism, intellect and also the unmanifested (mūla prakṛti), the ten senses and the one (the mind) and the five objects of the senses . . .

इच्छा द्वेषः सुखं दुःखं सङ्घातश्चेतना धृतिः ।
एतत्क्षेत्रं समासेन सविकारमुदाहृतम् ॥ १३·७ ॥
*icchā dveṣaḥ sukhaṁ duḥkhaṁ saṅghātaścetanā dhṛtiḥ,*
*etatkṣetraṁ samāsena savikāramudāhṛtam.* (13.7)

13.7 Desire, hatred, pleasure, pain, aggregate (body), intelligence, fortitude – this kṣetra has been thus briefly described with its modifications.

Contd.........

The 24 principles are:

The five great elements:

1. earth (pṛthvi),

2. water (āpa),

---

Contd..........

अमानित्वमदम्भित्वमहिंसा क्षान्तिरार्जवम् ।
आचार्योपासनं शौचं स्थैर्यमात्मविनिग्रहः ॥ १३·८ ॥

*amānitvamadambhitvamahiṁsā kṣāntirārjavam,*
*ācāryopāsanaṁ śoucaṁ sthairyamātmavinigrahaḥ.* (13.8)

13.8 Humility, unpretentiousness, non-injury, forgiveness, uprightness, service to the teacher, purity, steadfastness, self-control...

इन्दियार्थेषु वैराग्यमनहङ्कार एव च ।
जन्ममृत्युजराव्याधिदुःखदोषानुदर्शनम् ॥ १३·९ ॥

*indiyārtheṣu vairāgyamanahaṅkāra eva ca,*
*janmamṛtyujarāvyādhiduḥkhadoṣānudarśanam.* (13.9)

13.9 Indifference to the objects of the senses and also absence of egoism, perception of (or reflection upon) evils in birth, death, old age, sickness and pain.....

असक्तिरनभिष्वङ्गः पुत्रदारगृहादिषु ।
नित्यं च समचित्तत्वमिष्टानिष्टोपपत्तिषु ॥ १३·१० ॥

*asaktiranabhiṣvaṅgaḥ putradāragṛhādiṣu,*
*nityaṁ ca samacittatvamiṣṭāniṣṭopapattiṣu.* (13.10)

13.10 Non-attachment; non-identification of Self with son, wife, home and the rest; and constant even-mindedness on the attainment of the desirable and the undesirable...

मयि चानन्ययोगेन भक्तिरव्यभिचारिणी ।
विविक्तदेशसेवित्वमरतिर्जनसंसदि ॥ १३·११ ॥

*mayi cānanyayogena bhaktiravyabhicāriṇī,*
*viviktadeśasevitvamaratirjanasaṁsadi.* (13.11)

13.11 Unswerving devotion unto Me, by the yoga of non-separation, resorting to solitary places, distaste for the society of men...

3. fire (tejas),
4. wind (vāyu) and
5. space (Ākāśa).

The five organs of perception:

6. nose,
7. tongue,
8. eyes,
9. skin,
10. ears.

The five organs of action:

11. vocal chord,
12. legs,
13. hands,
14. genital organs,
15. anus.

The five objects of the senses:

16. smell,
17. taste,
18. form,
19. touch,
20. sound.

The four componants of antaḥkaraṇa are:

21. mind,
22. intellect,
23. ego,
24. citta.

The seven modifications of these 24 tattvas:

25. desire,
26. hatred,
27. pleasure,
28. pain,
29. the assembled body,
30. intelligence and
31. fortitude.

All these thirty one items put together constitute the field of experience.

> [Twenty virtues of sincere student of the right Knowledge: without these the seeker will not be able to detect and understand the divinity within matter that makes matter thrilled to dance in actions.]

1. humility
2. unpretentiousness

3. non-injury
4. forgiveness
5. uprightness
6. service to the teacher
7. purity of thoughts
8. steadfastness in following the right path in spite of obstacles en route
9. self-control
10. detachment from the objects of the senses
11. absence of egoism
12. recognising with disgust the evils of birth, death, old age, sickness and pain in life
13. non-attachment
14. absence of excessive love for those who depend upon you (son), those on whom you depend (wife), and your possessions which give security to you (house, etc.)
15. even mindedness in successes and disappointments
16. unfaltering devotion for Me
17. love for solitude

18. dislike for crowded noisy company
19. addiction to the knowldege of the Self and
20. understanding the end of true Knowledge to be Liberation.

These are the twenty virtues of a sincere seeker. These virtues together may be termed as 'knowledge' (jñānam) because a mind perfected with the above virtues is the vehicle through which the seeker can easily reach his destination, true Knowledge. A vehicle is often named by its very destination. Ignorance (ajñānam) is just the opposite of these virtues.

What should be realised is the great Truth, the Paramātman. It is the ultimate goal of knowledge. This knowledge about the Lord yields immortality to the realised devotee.

Paramātman, the highest God is beginningless. He existed even before time came into being. He is both existent and non-existent. He is existent because His presence is felt as the individuality (jīvātmā) in every body but at the same time He is generally considered as non-existent since He is not to be readily seen as the objects are seen and experienced.

['To define God is to defile God'. How can we, finite and imperfect creatures, define the infinite and the perfect God! Our knowledge, our power to express, our abilities in any field of knowledge are all finite in nature. So, an attempt to describe Him will definitely be a failure. We will surely land in ridiculous and ludicrous contradictions and hopeless inconsistencies. Still there is no harm in trying. If there is enough devotion in us, from the words of the Lord we can come to gain a fair idea of the true nature of Kṛṣṇa, the Supreme.]

God seems to have hands, feet, eyes, ears, heads and mouths on all sides and naturally so, because is He not everywhere, and is He not the one Life that functions through every limb?

The immortal Paramātman manifesting as jīvātmā in bodies gives power to the sense organs to function properly.[1]

But He is sans sense organs. He stands detached, and yet He supports and guards all. He is not endowed

[1] It is the presence of God as the individual soul that makes the eyes see, the ears hear, the nose smell, the tongue taste and the skin feel the touch respectively. It is He alone who gives power for the legs and hands and so on to move and lift. It is He who gives the power to speak, to feel and to think.

with the three guṇas but He, as the jīvātmā in each body seems to experience the fruits of all actions, which are prompted by the three guṇas of prakṛti.

God is everywhere. He is inside all beings as well as outside them. He is present in the movables and in the immovables. He is subtle. He is unknowable – cannot be known by the intellect as an object other than oneself. He is here, He is there, He is close by and He is also far away.

Again, He seems to be near – within the reach of the devoted intellect to the wise, but He is far away – beyond their conception to the ignorant.

He is really the undivided whole, but He seems to be divided, since He shines through all the different objects and beings.

He is the one Creator in the beginning, the one Protecter in the interval and the one Destroyer in the end.

He is pure effulgence. He is the effulgence of the effulgent ones; He is knowledge, the light. He is beyond the darkness of ignorance.

He is knowledge,[1] He is the object of knowledge[2]. He can be understood and realised only by knowledge. His shrine is within – in the heart itself.

I have explained to you clearly the kṣetra, the kṣetrajña and the Paramātman. My devotee who comprehends this becomes one with Me.

> [Puruṣa and prakṛti. What are they? What is their relationship with each other? How do they function?]

I told you earlier[3] that I express in My two aspects or natures – The higher (parā) and the lower (aparā). The former is otherwise known as Puruṣa or Kṣetrajña and the latter as prakṛti or the kṣetra. Since I am eternal and beginningless, My two natures are also eternal and beginningless (relatively).

Puruṣa remains ever changeless whereas all the modifications and experiences[4] such as pain and pleasure, spring from My prakṛti only.

---

1 20 virtues described earlier. The heart of such a man is God.

2 Lord the Supreme is to be experienced with the heart so trained and purified.

3 Chapter 7.

4 Refer the seven modifications enumerated in *Gītā* 13.6 & 13.7

It is prakṛti that produced the world of matter consisting of the 24 effects, such as the five elements, the ten sense organs, the mind, the intellect and the egoism, the unmanifest and the five sense of objects.

But the Puruṣa, (the jīvātmā or the kṣetrajña) residing in the body seems to experience pain and pleasure. Thus, the destiny of the Puruṣa in the body seems to be decided by the condition of the prakṛti. This is the mystery the ever pure Puruṣa comes to play as the jīvātmā in us and apparently undergoes various births and sufferings as determined by the past actions of the prakṛti aspect in each one of us.

> [kṣetrajña-jīvātmā – His real status, body, individuality, and the Supreme – Their relationship to each other – Who's who among them? – Why seek this knowledge? – The three paths to It.]

The jīvātmā, in an individual's body is a manifestation of the Paramātman. The former seems to be affected and conditioned by the good and evil actions performed by the body whereas the latter (Paramātman) stands unperturbed and untouched. Correctly speaking, the jīvātmā also is not at all affected by the body's experiences. He is just an onlooker; but due to its identification with the prakṛti it comes to experience the imperfections of the matter clothings around It.

The one who knows the kṣetra, with all its modifications, its exact relationship with the individual soul (jīvātmā), as also a relationship between the individual soul (jīvātman) and the supreme Soul (paramātman) knows everything that is fit to be known. This is the highest knowledge that promises immortality. Once a seeker realises that these three are all one immutable Reality, ever one with his own Self, he becomes Brahman.

Three paths running almost parallel to each other, but ultimately running into the one main approach road, which leads to the final experience of Paramātman are: 1. Meditation (dhyāna), 2. Study of the scriptures (jñāna) and 3. Selfless dedicated service (karma). Even those who are not very clever to follow any of these three paths can also achieve the Liberation of their personality from the shackles of their own false notions and stupid values, provided they fully understand the spiritual instructions taught by an able teacher (Guru) and they regularly worship God with devotion as per his advice.

[The saṁsāra; the world of objects and beings and all experiences of a man living his daily life.]

The saṁsāra, this world of animate and inanimate beings, is the offspring of the union between the prakṛti and the Puruṣa. Prakṛti (body) is perishable. The Puruṣa residing in the body (jīvātman) appears to undergo changes – birth and death. But the Paramātman is changeless and deathless.

One who can identify the individual self (jīvātmā) with the supreme Self (Paramātman) is qualified to enjoy immortality. In such an identification he understands the real status of Self, as a mere witness. Thereafter, the realised man is awakened to the experience that he is not injured by the injuries caused to his body.

All his actions are performed by the prakṛti only. One who understands that prakṛti alone is active, and that Puruṣa, the Self, as inactive, and is a mere onlooker, he understands the Truth.

Self, the source of all-pervading, is One without a second, but appears as many, when manifested into its manifold forms.

The Self lends life to prakṛti, which thus getting animated, acts. Prakṛti acts due to the Self (Puruṣa) but Puruṣa though residing in prakṛti remains 'inactive'. Since the Self does not act, He does not acquire any vāsanās. The immutable Self thus remains ever changeless, ever immaculate and pure.

The Self cannot have any intimate relationship with anything else, for the simple reason that there is in the Self nothing other than the Self. The pure Self alone is; the world of objects, emotions and thoughts are the interpretations of the Self by the body, mind and intellect in us.

The Self is like the all-pervading space, which is ever in contact with objects and yet is not contaminated by those things just as the one sun illumines the entire world of objects, so also does the Self illumine all perceptions and all experiences. As consciousness in us, it is the Self that illumines all our experiences.

The vision of wisdom will enable one to distinguish between the kṣetra and the Kṣetrajña – the prakṛti and the Puruṣa – and this understanding helps one to liberate oneself from the shackles of prakṛti and reach to realise the supreme state of Paramātman".

---

अध्यात्मज्ञाननित्यत्वं तत्त्वज्ञानार्थदर्शनम् ।
एतज्ज्ञानमिति प्रोक्तमज्ञानं यदतोऽन्यथा ॥ १३·१२ ॥

*adhyātmajñānanityatvaṁ tattvajñānārthadarśanam,*
*etajjñānamiti proktamajñānaṁ yadato'nyathā.* (13.12)

12. Constancy in Self-knowledge, perception of the end of true Knowledge; this is declared to be Knowledge, and what is opposed to it is ignorance.

ज्ञेयं यत्तत्प्रवक्ष्यामि यज्ज्ञात्वामृतमश्नुते ।
अनादिमत्परं ब्रह्म न सत्तन्नासदुच्यते ॥ १३·१३ ॥

*jñeyaṁ yattatpravakṣyāmi yajjñātvāmṛtamaśnute,*
*anādimatparaṁ brahma na sattannāsaducyate.* (13.13)

13.13. I will now declare, that which has to be known, knowing which one attains to immortality, the beginningless supreme Brahman, called neither being nor non-being.

सर्वतःपाणिपादं तत्सर्वतोऽक्षिशिरोमुखम् ।
सर्वतःश्रुतिमल्लोके सर्वमावृत्य तिष्ठति ॥ १३·१४ ॥

*sarvataḥpāṇipādaṁ tatsarvato'kṣiśiromukham,*
*sarvataḥśrutimalloke sarvamāvṛtya tiṣṭhati.* (13.14)

13.14. With hands and feet everywhere, with eyes, heads and mouths everywhere, with ears everywhere, He exists in the world, enveloping all.

पुरुषः प्रकृतिस्थो हि भुङ्क्ते प्रकृतिजान्गुणान् ।
कारणं गुणसङ्गोऽस्य सदसद्योनिजन्मसु ॥ १३·२२ ॥

*puruṣaḥ prakṛtistho hi bhuṅkte prakṛtijānguṇān,*
*kāraṇaṁ guṇasaṅgo'sya sadasadyonijanmasu.* (13.22)

13.22. Puruṣa seated in prakṛti, experiences the qualities born of prakṛti; attachment to the qualities is the cause of his birth in good and evil wombs.

---

**Questions on chapter XIII**

1. What were the questions Arjuna asked in the opening stanza of the 13th chapter of *Gītā*? (1)
2. Why is the body called the 'kṣetra – the field'? What constitute the 'field' ? (2)
3. Who is the 'Knower of the field'? (2)
4. What is 'Knowledge'? (3)

5. What all constitute the 'field'? (6-7)

6. What do you understand by 'Ananya-yoga'? (11)

7. What is jñānam? (8-12)

8. What is it that 'ought to be known'? (13-18)

9. What are the modifications and qualities born out of prakṛti? (20-22)

10. When the equipments are caused by prakṛti, how is it that the Puruṣa is said to be the experience? (21)

11. What do we mean when śāstras say "Paramātman is in this body?" (23)

12. Who are said to be the true seers of the universe? (29-34)

13. With the eye of wisdom what exactly does he subtly perceive? (35)

# Chapter XIV

## Guṇatraya-vibhāga-yoga

(Yoga of Three Guṇas)

[The three guṇas – The entire humanity can be broadly classified into three types based on the preponderance in them of the qualities of sattva, rajas or tamas – The idea that the prakṛti seems to decide the destiny of the Puruṣa is made clearer. The behaviour of a person is indicated by the proportion of sattva, rajas and tamas in personality. When one learns that he is the Self within, ever a spectator alone of the behaviours of the body, and not the body itself, and so does not throw his lot with that of the body, there is nothing more to learn.]

Arjuna: "In spite of one single Spirit, standing as the common substratum of all and in spite of the body having the same elements in its make-up in all, do we not Kṛṣṇa, find numerous varieties of persons? How can we explain this experience of plurality?"

Lord Kṛṣṇa: "Let me tell you at the outset that prakṛti is the active mother, and I, the supreme Puruṣa, is the unactive father. The entire universe of animate and inanimate beings is born to us, the divine father and mother.

A child generally inherits the qualities of both mother and father. The living beings, our own children, however, unfortunately borrow mostly the qualities of their mother and very seldom the perfections of Me, their father.

There are three guṇas: the three temperaments under which every creature functions. They are (1) sattva (perfect purity), 2. rajas (passion), 3. tamas (inertia). Though these are born of prakṛti, they apparently bind the Spirit within and when the Spirit identifies itself with the prakṛti, It becomes a Puruṣa.

When a person is influenced mostly by the pure sattva no evil thought enters his mind. No crime is committed by him. He experiences only happiness. He thirsts only for the right knowledge.

When a person is influenced mostly by rajas, he is full of passion, which breeds desires to possess things, and attachments to the possessions. He is then always immersed in activities which help to fulfil his wishes.

When a person is under the influence of tamas, he has no noble instincts and wallows in the darkness of ignorance and laziness. He does not live; he only exists.

Sattva goads one to seek happiness in higher things; rajas prompts one into activities to gain material happiness, while tamas makes one careless and negligent.

A person is said to be sāttvika (noble, pure) when he conquers rajas and tamas to certain extent; he is rājasika when this quality predominates over the sattva and tamas in him, and he is tāmasika when he has a greater share of tamas than sattva and rajas in him.

[Signs of these guṇas – sattva, rajas and tamas – and the destiny of the three types – the sāttvika, the rājasika and the tāmasika.]

A sāttvika one has a keen, penetrating intelligence. He sees, hears and understands rightly. The perfection of knowledge will be as it were glittering about all expressions of his personality.

There is love in his movements, tenderness in his feelings, brilliant tranquility in his thinking.

A sāttvika man, at his death, leaves here to reach and enjoy happiness in heaven. Since he has harboured only good thoughts in his mind and performed only good actions, he reaps, naturally, a rich harvest of happiness.

A sāttvika person is noble in thoughts, words and deeds, wise in his judgements, and belongs to the glorious type.

A rājasika man is one who is never content with what he has. He is always engaged in such activities as would help him to aggrandise more and more wealth. Because of his desire for wealth and attachment to it, he knows no peace of mind either.

After his death, he is reborn in the world among men, having similar tastes and engaged in the same activities.

Since his actions are motivated by desires and since it is humanly impossible to satisfy all desires, he reaps pain and discontentment. He is greedy to grab more and hoard, and this is the picture of an ordinary man of the world. A tāmasika man is dull in intelligence, inert, negligent, careless – in short, he is capable of making only mistakes.

After his death, he goes to hell as he is enveloped by foul ignorance, and he suffers therein untold miseries and tortures. Then he is reborn in the world in the lowest of species.

Since he is ignorant of the good values of life and does not make any attempt to improve himself, he reaps only the fruits of ignorance – pain and sorrow.

From what I have told you, it must be clear that there is no active agent other than the guṇas. The Self is not the agent of any action – good, bad or indifferent. A man suffers because he identifies himself with his body, and with its experiences such as birth, growth, decay, disease and death. A wise man identifies himself with his Self and is, therefore, beyond all the three guṇas. Hence he suffers not the pangs of such experiences".

[guṇātīta: One who has transcended the three guṇas – His distinguishing characteristics – His conduct among others – How can one come to the state of guṇātīta.]

Arjuna: "Tell me the distinguishing marks of a man, not bound by the three guṇas. How does he behave? How does he conquer these guṇas?"

Lord Kṛṣṇa : A sāttvika man would love solitude and seek knowledge while a rājasika one would love to act for material gains. A tāmasika person, however, would wait for happiness to reach him, without any effort on his part; 'minimum work and maximum gains' is his false and stupid philosophy.

But a guṇātīta is above all these, and he is not bound by any of these considerations. He is so perfectly balanced in mind that he does neither love nor hate solitude. He does not love action and is not averse to it. With this condition of masterly self-sufficiency he remains in his own nature.[1]

The guṇātīta is a sthitaprajña, whom I pointed out before. He is not moved in the least, by what happens around him or to his body, because all the changes he sees, apply only to the matter vehicles in him. He knows that changes are inevitable and are due to the working of the three guṇas. In his spiritual experience he has become the Spirit in essence. How

1 Already described in chapter 2.

can the Spirit be affected in any way by the change occurring in matter!

He keeps his balance of mind and is content always. He accepts pain and pleasure, sand and gold, success and disappointment, praise and censure, honour and insult in the same detached way. He does not love the one more that befriends him nor the one less who injures him. He turns away from selfish activities and works for the good of humanity, always considering himself only as an agent of God.

This is made possible, because he loves God so much that he has become one with Him and accepts pain and pleasure as gifts from Him.

Stopping all selfish activities, he who serves Me with love in thought, word and deed transcends the limitations of the guṇas. He gains complete freedom from all his mortal limitations, mokṣa. He becomes one with Me".

---

### Questions on Chapter XIV

1. What are the three guṇas? (5)

2. What happens when a person is influenced by sattva, rajas and tamas? (Give the answers in separate paragraphs). (6-9)
3. "It becomes Puruṣa". – What and when? (5)
4. What are the qualities of a sāttvika person? (6)
5. What are the signs of a rājasika person? (7)
6. "He reaps only the fruits of ignorance". – explain. (8)
7. What are the causes of sufferings? (9-13)
8. "He suffers not the pangs of such experiences". – Who and why? (19, 20)
9. What do you mean by guṇātīta? – Explain. (22, 23)
10. What are the distinguishing characteristics of a guṇātīta? (24)
11. How can one attain the state of guṇātīta? (25)
12. "He becomes one with Me". – Explain with reference to the context. (26)

# Chapter XV

## Puruṣottama-yoga

(Yoga of Supreme Spirit)

[One who knows that Paramātmā, the Puruṣottama, is higher than the perishable and the imperishable puruṣas, is the wisest.]

(This chapter is generally sung by Hindus before they take their food).

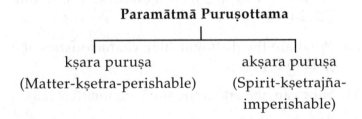

**Paramātmā Puruṣottama**

| kṣara puruṣa | akṣara puruṣa |
|---|---|
| (Matter-kṣetra-perishable) | (Spirit-kṣetrajña-imperishable) |

Lord Kṛṣṇa: "From what I have told you so far, you would have gathered that this world is perishable, changing, false, unreal and imperfect in every way. A mortal, being a mixture of imperfect matter and perfect Spirit, has evil as well as good instincts. The good instincts propel him towards God while his bad instincts drag him down into the mire of worldly existence. The alluring objects beckon him from all sides. The poor mortal is trapped by them. The three guṇas (sattva, rajas and tamas) also contribute their share to his downfall and get him more and more caught up in the cycle of birth, growth, decay, disease and death. The ignorant man runs towards the world's superficial attractions and glamour to embrace, in effect, its agonies while the wise man runs away from them in search of God.

The world can be figuratively spoken of as a pipal tree (aśvattha), which can be cut down by the axe of steady and firm non-attachment. The only way to escape from this miserable existence to a world of peace and happiness is to cultivate detachment by watching closely and recognising fully the imperfections of the world of gratifications. A deep study of the Vedas gives a clear vision of the life here and of the life hereafter. One has to retire fully from one's attractions and hungers to enjoy this world, before one seeks the realm of God. He should rise above pride, delusion, attachment to kith and kin, desires to acquire and to hoard, pain and pleasure which are the features of worldly existence, and only then can he concentrate fully and efficiently upon the realisation of God.

The realm of God is real and attractive. The world of mortals is false and ugly. The effulgent sun, moon and fire cannot bring light to illumine the seat of the Lord, because It is always brighter than these. Every mortal should strive to reach this immortal kingdom and learn to stay there.

[jīvātmā: The individual soul; its enjoyment of the world of objects.]

The individual soul (jīva) residing in the body is an imaginary portion of My indivisible Self. It attracts to itself all the five organs of perception, and the mind, and with these it enjoys the world of objects. This individual soul then moves on from body to body, from birth to birth, carrying with it the impressions left by its previous actions and experiences. This movement of the jīva from body to body can be compared with the wind that moves from place to place gathering the scent of flowers. Apparently, it is the individual soul (jīva) then, that is said to 'enjoy the world' with its five sense organs and the mind. The 'individuality'(jīva) in us is the 'experiencer' of all our joys and sorrows.[1]

The Lord thus seated within everyone, at all times and acting as though He is endowed with the three guṇas is always invisible to the ignorant – at birth, at death and during life – because he is always engrossed in the attraction of the world and has no eyes to see the presence of the Lord within himself.[2]

Mere wishful thinking and a mechanical spiritual routine of prayer and meditation are not sufficient to transport one to the realm of God. Steady contemplation with a thorough and correct knowledge of God alone can take one to Him.

---

1 कार्यकारणकर्तृत्वे हेतुः प्रकृतिरुच्यते ।
पुरुषः सुखदुःखानां भोक्तृत्वे हेतुरुच्यते ॥ १३·२१ ॥
*kāryakāraṇakartṛtve hetuḥ prakṛtirucyate,*
*puruṣaḥ sukhaduḥkhānāṁ bhoktṛtve heturucyate.* (13.21)

13.21. In the production of the effect and the cause, prakṛti is said to be the cause; in the experience of pleasure and pain, Puruṣa is said to be the cause.

2 Note Vibhūti-yoga, chapter 10.41.

## The glories of God

[How can we indicate what exactly is the nature, power and function of God – where can we detect Him expressing Himself in our own life and around us.]

I am the sunlight in the sun, the moonlight in the moon, and the heat in the fire. I am the fertility of the soil and the nourishing and curative power of plants and herbs. I am also the digestive power of living beings, taking from all types of food[1] the nourishing part and throwing away – ejecting – the unwanted part.

I am seated in the shrine of the heart of all beings. Memory, knowledge and forgetfulness spring from Me alone. I am the theme of all the Vedas; the very author of the Vedānta, and the Knower of the three Vedas – the *Ṛg-veda,* the *Yajur-veda* and the *Sāma-veda.*

In the world, you see My two forms; 1. The Kṣara (the perishable, the matter), and 2. The Akṣara (the Imperishable; the Spirit). All the perishable objects are my perishable form: and the Self, the ray of God

[1] Note the four types of food: (1) masticated; (2) swallowed; (3) sucked; and (4) licked

functioning in us as the life seated in the heart of all is My imperishable form .

The Supreme is distinct from these two and is called Paramātmā, who pervades and supports all the three worlds – the three fields of experiences the waking, dream and dreamless sleep. I am well known in the Vedas as Puruṣottama because I am the best, supreme, highest (uttama), and above the perishable puruṣa.

That wise man, who, ignoring all his enchantments or his physical body, strives to know Me as Puruṣottama, is one who has fulfilled his mission in life".

---

न तद्भासयते सूर्यो न शशाङ्को न पावकः ।
यद्गत्वा न निवर्तन्ते तद्धाम परमं मम ॥ १५·६ ॥

*na tadbhāsayate sūryo na śaśāṅko na pāvakaḥ,*
*yadgatvā na nivartante taddhāma paramaṁ mama.* (15.6)

15.6 Nor does the sun shine there, nor moon, nor fire; to which having gone they return not; that is My supreme abode.

यतन्तो योगिनश्चैनं पश्यन्त्यात्मन्यवस्थितम्।
यतन्तोऽप्यकृतात्मानो नैनं पश्यन्त्यचेतसः॥ १५·११॥

*yatanto yoginaścainaṁ paśyantyātmanyavasthitam,*
*yatanto'pyakṛtātmāno nainaṁ paśyantyacetasaḥ.* (15.11)

15.11 The seekers striving (for perfection) behold Him dwelling in the Self; but the unrefined and unintelligent, even though striving, see Him not.

यदादित्यगतं तेजो जगद्भासयतेऽखिलम्।
यच्चन्द्रमसि यच्चाग्नौ तत्तेजो विद्धि मामकम्॥ १५·१२॥

*yadādityagataṁ tejo jagadbhāsayate'khilam,*
*yaccandramasi yaccāgnau tattejo viddhi māmakam.* (15.12)

15.12. The light which is residing in the sun illumines the whole world, and that which is in the moon and in the fire, know that light to be Mine.

गामाविश्य च भूतानि धारयाम्यहमोजसा।
पुष्णामि चौषधीः सर्वाः सोमो भूत्वा रसात्मकः॥ १५·१३॥

*gāmāviśya ca bhūtāni dhārayāmyahamojasā,*
*puṣṇāmi cauṣadhīḥ sarvāḥ somo bhūtvā rasātmakaḥ.* (15.13)

15.13. Permeating the earth I support all beings by (My) energy; and having become the juicy moon I nourish all herbs.

अहं वैश्वानरो भूत्वा प्राणिनां देहमाश्रितः ।
प्राणापानसमायुक्तः पचाम्यन्नं चतुर्विधम् ॥ (१५·१४)

*ahaṁ vaiśvānaro bhūtvā prāṇināṁ dehamāśritaḥ,*
*prāṇāpānasamāyuktaḥ pacāmyannaṁ caturvidham.* (15.14)

15.14 I, having become (the fire) Vaiśvānara, abide in the body of beings, and associated with prāṇa and apāna digest the fourfold food.

उत्तमः पुरुषस्त्वन्यः परमात्मेत्युदाहृतः ।
यो लोकत्रयमाविश्य बिभर्त्यव्यय ईश्वरः ॥ १५·१७ ॥

*uttamaḥ puruṣastvanyaḥ paramātmetyudāhṛtaḥ,*
*yo lokatrayamāviśya bibhartyavyaya īśvaraḥ.* (15.17)

15.17 But distinct is the supreme Puruṣa called the highest Self, the indestructible Lord, who pervading the three worlds (waking, dream and deep sleep), sustains them.

---

## Questions on Chapter XV

1. "The poor mortal is trapped by them". – By what? (1,7)
2. What are the contributions of the three guṇas towards the destruction of men?(2)

3. Describe the difference between a wise and a bad man. (16)

4. How can a man concentrate fully and efficiently upon the Realisation of God? (4-5)

5. "It is always bright". – Explain. (12)

6. Give a brief description of the 'experiencer' of all our joys and sorrows. (19)

7. How can a man reach God? (5)

8. Write short notes on the following:

   (1) kṣara (the perishable). (16)

   (2) akṣara (the Imperishable) (16)

   (3) Paramātmā (17)

# Chapter XVI

## Daivāsura-sampad-vibhāga-yoga

(Yoga of Divine and Devilish Estates)

[This chapter gives a detailed description of two types of personalities: (1) the sāttvika, the daivika – the godly, the heavenly; (2) the rājasika, the āsurika – the devilish, earthly. It mentions the three great vices (1) desire (kāma), (2) anger (krodha) and (3) greed (lobha) which are to be conquered. It concludes with an advice to follow the rules laid down in the scriptures.]

Arjuna: "Tell me, Kṛṣṇa, more about the sāttvika and the rājasika personalities and also show me how a rājasika man can conquer his evil instincts and become a sāttvika personality".

[The wealth of the divinely good – sāttvika – The inner wealth of personality – a wealth of intellectual power and moral strength.]

Lord Kṛṣṇa: "The sāttvika, meaning the noble and the cultured is the one who possesses the 26 brilliant virtues. These are inherent in him. He finds these, in himself in plenty. They are: 1. Fearlessness to meet the ups and the downs of life and the heroism to pursue a noble ideal inspite of adverse criticisms; 2. Purity in thought; 3. Thirst to know God; 4. Gift of wealth, love, service or knowledge and so on to the deserving and the needy; 5. Control over the senses in the midst of temptations; 6. Selfless for the welfare of humanity; 7. A thorough knowledge of the scriptures; 8. Austerity (tapas); 9. Uprightness to live up to the ideal preached; 10. Non-injury, in thoughts, words and deeds; 11. Truthfulness to one's own convictions; 12. Angerlessness, even when provoked; 13. Renunciation; 14. Tranquillity of mind; 15. Absence of malice (sweet in speech); 16. Kindness to all; 17. Not coveting other's goods and wordly pleasures; 18. Gentleness; 19. Not displaying his wealth, his knowledge, his power and so on; 20. Absence of fickleness and restlessness; 21. Efficiency (outshining others in all fields of activities); 22. Capacity to forgive even those who harm him; 23. Fortitude, to bounce up again, inspite of failures and fight again with the fresh challenges of life;

24. Physically clean and mentally pure; 25. Absence of hatred even in thought; 26. Absence of pride (pride arises out of an exaggerated opinion of oneself).

These virtues are the real inexhaustible wealth of a noble and cultured man. He is divinely sweet, and is fit to enter the kingdom of God.

> [The wealth of a diabolically fallen man (āsurika or rājasika).The mental perversions and the natural sorrows – a low type of personality comes to suffer – The consequent inefficiencies in him.]

I shall now give you an estimate of the inner rubbish of an uncultured, unrefined man of the world. 1. Ostentatiousness – acting the part of a greater man than he really is, meaning hypocrisy; 2. Arrogance – looking down upon others; 3. Self-conceit; 4. Fury, wrath; 5. Harshness in words and in deeds; 6. Ignorance of his own real vicious nature.

These are the vices ordinarily possessed by a man of the world. He is really a devil, stalking on two legs – an abominable specimen of humanity. Undoubtedly these vices drag one to hell.

Now, Arjuna, this 'devil in human form' need not lose hope, provided he develops a tendency to shed his vices. This devil-man can convert himself into a God-man by the sheer strength of his mind and sincere right effort.

These vile men do not know what is right and what is wrong. So, they not only omit to do the right thing but commit the wrongs. They are physically unclean and mentally filthy. They are strangers to good conduct.

They are true neither to themselves nor to others. What they think, they do not preach; what they preach, they do not practise either. The result is that they become a miserable mixture of contradictions.

They fail to see the glory of God in anything in the world, in its creation and in its destruction. They fail to recognise and refuse to accept the supreme power that supports it. They are blind to the eternal law behind all the marvellous systematic changes that take place in the world. More than that, they even vehemently deny the very existence of God!

To them, the world is the product of lust and the desires of men and women. How can they see anything glorious and divine in such a filthy world? Impossible indeed.

Holding thus the view that the world comes out of nothing and would end in nothing, they make the most of their present existence by seeking only sensual pleasures. Since they do not have any inspiring and noble ideals to cling to, they do not hesitate to do fierce and frightful deeds. They distribute nothing but dejection and disaster everywhere. They are the greatest enemies of the world. Not only they bring ruin upon themselves but they drag others also along with them.

With an insatiable lust and desire, full of hypocrisy, conceit and arrogance they put into practice their foul resolves. They cannot find any rhythm or harmony around or within themselves.

They have come to the conclusion that the present existence is the be-all and end-all of achievements. They do not believe in life after death. Thus they drag on their existence till death, with cares and anxieties as their constant companions – a burden to themselves and a nuisance to others. Their life is a perfect tragedy filled with sobs and sorrows.

To appease their hunger for earthly pleasures, they direct all their energies to amass wealth by foul means. The end, to them, justifies the means.

Their ignorance and delusion knows no bounds. Whether it is wealth or power, they are never content with what they have or what they get. Their whole attention is focused on the plans to acquire more. In short, in their vanity, they consider themselves supreme and all-powerful. In their opinion, they are miniature Gods. They attach to themselves all the glorious attributes of God. In their estimate of themselves there is no one equal to them, either in nobility of birth or in wealth.

In the display of their wealth and power, they expose actually their basest animal nature. They pose themselves as generous and pious, because they want their fame and name to be sung by others. Bewildered and blinded by such fancies, they live a shameless and ignoble life and thus make a direct suicidal dash to hell itself.

Endowed with egoism, brutal strength, arrogance, lust and anger, these malicious men are really lower and baser than the wild beasts. They hate God and are jealous of godly men. These lowly and base creatures court their degeneration and downfall by such sinful actions. Naturally, it is just for Me to throw them into hell and torture them continuously. They are again born into the mortal world in filthy surroundings. They drift farther and farther away from Me in every birth and finally fall into the deep and dark abyss of hell.

[The three gateways to hell – how a rājasika man can become sāttvika.]

Desire, anger and avarice are the three gateways to hell. So, those who want to improve themselves and rise up higher – to become sāttvika – should abandon these three vices. These are the deadly enemies of men. If mortals can conquer these three foes by intelligent effort they can surely attain salvation. But those who live with no noble ideal in life, ignoring the rules laid down in the scriptures for proper conduct, come to court ruin in the end.

Therefore, dear Pārtha, find out first what is right and what is wrong from the scriptures. Then plan your life and conduct yourself accordingly. In this dreary forest of life, in the jungle of its challenges, infested by the ferocious beasts of its irresistible desires, the knowledge of the scriptures is the beacon light to guide you safely to your destination".

---

अहिंसा सत्यमक्रोधस्त्यागः शान्तिरपैशुनम् ।
दया भूतेष्वलोलुप्त्वं मार्दवं ह्रीरचापलम् ॥ १६·२ ॥

*ahiṁsā satyamakrodhastyāgaḥ śāntirapaiśunam,*
*dayā bhūteṣvaloluptvaṁ mārdavaṁ hrīracāpalam.* (16.2)

16.2 Harmlessness, truth, absence of anger, renunciation, peacefulness, absence of crookedness, compassion to beings, uncovetousness, gentleness, modesty, absence of fickleness.

तेजः क्षमा धृतिः शौचमद्रोहो नातिमानिता ।
भवन्ति सम्पदं दैवीमभिजातस्य भारत ॥ १६·३ ॥

*tejaḥ kṣamā dhṛtiḥ śaucamadroho nātimānitā,*
*bhavanti sampadaṁ daivīmabhijātasya bhārata.* (16.3)

16.3 Vigour, forgiveness, fortitude, purity, absence of hatred, absence of pride – these belong to the one born for the divine estate, O Bhārata.

त्रिविधं नरकस्येदं द्वारं नाशनमात्मनः ।
कामः क्रोधस्तथा लोभस्तस्मादेतत्त्रयं त्यजेत् ॥ १६·२१ ॥

*trividhaṁ narakasyedaṁ dvāraṁ nāśanamātmanaḥ,*
*kāmaḥ krodhastathā lobhastasmādetattrayaṁ tyajet.* (16.21)

16.21. Triple is the gate of this hell, destructive of the self – lust, anger and greed. Therefore, one should abandon these three.

एतैर्विमुक्तः कौन्तेय तमोद्वारैस्त्रिभिर्नरः ।
आचरत्यात्मनः श्रेयस्ततो याति परां गतिम् ॥ १६·२२ ॥

*etairvimuktaḥ kaunteya tamodvāraistribhirnaraḥ,*
*ācaratyātmanaḥ śreyastato yāti parāṁ gatim.* (16.22)

16.22 A man who is liberated from these three gates to darkness, O Kaunteya, practises what is good for him and thus goes to the supreme goal.

## Questions on Chapter XVI

1. Explain any three qualities of the 'divinely good'. (1,2)

2. 'Nātimānitā' means something more than 'absence of pride'. What is it? (3)

3. Explain any three qualities of the 'diabolically fallen'. (4,5)

4. Lord Kṛṣṇa says that He has described divine qualities at length earlier. Mention the chapter and verses where He has explained?

5. How do the 'demonic people view life? (7,8)

6. What is the ultimate end of such demonic people in their life? (9-16)

7. What are three major factors responsible for destruction of the self? (21)

8. What a man should do if he has to attain the supreme Goal? (22)

9. After giving the description of two types of people, what is the conclusion drawn in this chapter? (24)

# Chapter XVII

## Śraddhātraya – vibhāga – yoga

(Yoga of Threefold Faith)

[One of the most exhaustive and powerful chapters or stanzas. Here, we get an exhaustive explanation of sattva, rajas and tamas as influencing men in the choice of their goal in life, food, sacrifices and self-control.]

Arjuna: "Kṛṣṇa, what will happen to those who do not follow the instructions on how to live as contained in the scriptures, but strive hard pouring forth the best in them in the service of the world (yajña)?

Kindly also tell me more concerning the sāttvika, the rājasika and the tāmasika men. Whom do they worship? What do they eat? In what type of activities are they interested in? What penances do they practise?"

Lord Kṛṣṇa: "I told you earlier in another context[1] that really speaking, the present birth is an

[1] Refer chapter 6.41 and 42

extension of the past birth and the jīvātmā is said to gather impression of action[1] in its progress from birth to birth. These impressions collected so far influence an individual's mode of life. His tastes in food, his bent in particular activities, and so on, are developed through successive births. No tendency or activity springs from us all of a sudden as an accident, independent of all previous causes.

A mortal cannot, all of a sudden in this birth take up to the study of the scriptures, develop a liking for the divine spiritual life, plan his life as per the rules prescribed in the scriptures and worship Me. He must have had developed slowly and gradually, through successive births, the tendency to undertake the spiritual pilgrimage.

Faith[2] (śraddhā) is the fruit of the vāsanās thus developed through births. It can be of three kinds: sāttvika (heavenly), the rājasika (earthly) and the

---

[1] Refer chapter 15.8

[2] The belief in what I do not know, so that I may come to know what I believe in is called faith. Faith is that towards which each of us irresistably gravitates in all our actions, feelings and thoughts. Thus, everyone of us has a goal, a great destination. This is the 'faith' in each one of us.

tāmasika (hellish). A man is, as his faith is; nay, man is but his faith.

In the choice of deities for worship, we find three distinct types of men. Men of heavenly faith worship the benevolent gods, while those of earthly faith propitiate the demi-gods of wealth and power and those of hellish faith court evil-spirits – the dead and the devils.

There are some, who, in their overenthusiasm to make soaring progress in religious life take the wrong turn to please Me. They, attracted still to the worldly pleasures, observe severe austerities to exhibit their false piety. They mortify their bodies by continued fasts and such other physical mortifications. Since they have not disciplined their mind well, these mechanical religious practices, instead of helping them, do damage to them. Moreover, they are really torturing Me by such foolish physical regimentation.

In the selection of food also we find three different tastes. The sāttvika people like substantially energy giving and tasty food which brings cheer and preserves health.

The rājasika men, however, like to eat bitter, sour, salty, excessively hot and fried things, which damage their health and bring sorrow to them in the long run.

The tāmasika ones like cold, preserved, tasteless and unclean food. They do not mind taking food with a strong smell and what is left over by others.

When one has a great goal in which one has full faith and one takes food and thus creates energy in oneself, the individual cannot but pour himself out through his faculties and abilities in order to achieve his goal. This outpouring into the field of actions is called yajña.

Sāttvika persons perform sacrifices as prescribed by the science of life (śāstras) and offer selfless service considering all activities to be their duty. There is thus an inner compulsion to act and achieve and they do not expect any reward in return other than the joy of doing it all entirely with an artist's satisfaction.

The rājasika perform sacrifices and many exhausting undertakings in the world to exhibit their wealth and position to obtain name and fame.

The tāmasika may perform religious rites but they are pursued mechanically without faith and their sacred rituals are so merely in name. They do not give away anything freely to any deserving person.

When one is fired by a faith and has energy gained through right type of food, one expresses oneself in action (yajña) bringing out one's abilities, capacities and faculties. But the success in life will depend not only upon the faculties you have brought into the field of action, but the consistency, dash, push, dynamism with which you have performed the yajñas.

There are three types of ascetics practising different types of tapas: physical (śarīra), verbal (vāṅgmaya) and mental (mānasa).

Physical penance consists of the worship of the gods, the men of wisdom (brāhmaṇas), the teachers and the wise; bodily cleanliness; straightforwardness; celibacy and non-injury.

Verbal penance is study of the Vedas and sweet speech, pleasing to all but conforming to truth.

Under mental penance comes cheerfulness of the mind, gentleness, silence, self-control and faultless conduct.

This threefold tapas, when practised with faith and conviction expecting nothing in return is sāttvika.

When this threefold tapas is practised to show off one's wealth and power, and to gain reputation and reverence from others, it is rājasika. Naturally, the reputation and reverence which they obtain from those can only be transient.

When the threefold tapas is observed without understanding its significance, but to torture oneself and others, it is tāmasika.

When energy gathered from food is poured out in yajña to reach the faith, and thus with a personality disciplined with tapas, we come to bless not only ourselves but also others around us, this is dāna (gift).

Gifts also fall under three classes, according to the predominant guṇa class to which the individual falls. A gift is sāttvika when it is given to the deserving and to the needy at the right time and at the right place, expecting no profit in return. A gift is rājasika when reluctantly given and that too with a selfish motive. A gift is tāmasika when it is thrown out to an unworthy recipient with contempt.

Om is the name of the Lord in His transcendental form; Tat is Lord in His universal form; Sat is Lord when He expresses His divinity through man's noble intentions and heroic actions. To remember, therefore, the Lord in these aspects as we do our actions (yajña, tapa or dāna) is to purify our work from any possible contaminations of rajas and tamas.

'Om Tat Sat' means, Lord Almighty is the only Reality. This mantra is so powerful that it removes all imperfections, in our actions or in our intentions. Therefore, it is advisable to give, to sacrifice and to perform penance or any auspicious act, uttering this mantra and thus keeping the Lord's remembrance in our mind. By that, the ego is completely forgotten. Only the Lord Almighty is continuously remembered and efficiently surrendered to. The devoted heart when chanting 'Om Tat Sat' consideres that all acts are done by His grace and all fruits of success and failure are given unto Him at His altar.

Sacrifice, charity and penance without a pure motive and faith are fruitless. They do not fetch any result now or later. Faith is the man; have a firm faith in a noble ideal and thus act tirelessly to achieve it in a spirit of dedication and love unto Him. To one, who works thus in the world, success is sure, Arjuna, there is no doubt about it".

---

देवद्विजगुरुप्राज्ञपूजनं शौचमार्जवम् ।
ब्रह्मचर्यमहिंसा च शारीरं तप उच्यते ॥ १७·१४ ॥

*devadvijagurupräjñapūjanaṁ śaucamārjavam,*
*brahmacaryamahiṁsā ca śārīraṁ tapa ucyate.* (17.14)

17.14 Worship of the gods, the twice-born, the teachers and the wise, purity, straightforwardness, celibacy, and non-injury are called the austerity of the body.

दातव्यमिति यद्दानं दीयतेऽनुपकारिणे ।
देशे काले च पात्रे च तद्दानं सात्विकं स्मृतम् ॥ १७·२० ॥

*dātavyamiti yaddānaṁ dīyate'nupakāriṇe,*
*deśe kāle ca pātre ca taddānaṁ sāttvikaṁ smṛtam.* (17.20)

17.20 That gift which is given to one who does nothing in return, knowing it to be a duty to give at a fit place and time to a worthy person, that gift is held to be sāttvika.

अश्रद्धया हुतं दत्तं तपस्तप्तं कृतं च यत्।
असदित्युच्यते पार्थ न च तत्प्रेत्य नो इह ॥ १७·२८ ॥

*aśraddhayā hutaṁ dattaṁ tapastaptaṁ kṛtaṁ ca yat,*
*asadityucyate pārtha na ca tatpretya no iha.* (17.28)

17.28. Whatever is sacrificed, given or performed and whatever austerity is practised without faith, it is called 'asat' O Pārtha; it is not here or hereafter (after death).

---

## Questions on Chapter XVII

1. "These impressions collected so far influence an individual's mode of life". – Explain. (2)
2. What is faith? (3,4)
3. Write short notes on: Men of 'heavenly faith'; Men of 'earthly faith'; Men of 'hellish faith'. (17-19)
4. "Moreover, they are really torturing Me". – Who, why and how? (5, 6)
5. Explain the food habits of the three different types of people. (8-10)

6. What do you mean by yajña? (11-13)
7. Explain the motives behind the three types of people in performing yajñas. (11-13)
8. What can we gain by tapas? (14-16)
9. What are the different types of tapas and how can a man become sāttvika, rājasika or tāmasika? (17-19)
10. Describe the three classes of dāna? (20-22)
11. "By that the ego is completely forgotten". – Explain. (23)
12. "There is no doubt about it". – About what? (27, 28)
13. "Om Tat Sat". – Explain (24-26)
14. What are the austerities of the body? (19)
15. "Tat dānam sāttvikam smṛta". – Which dāna? (20)

# Chapter XVIII

## Mokṣa – sannyāsa – yoga

(Yoga of Libration Though Renunciation)

[This concluding chapter is a general survey, almost a hasty revision of the instructions given so far, stressing upon the important points already mentioned. Here, the Lord presses out His entire divine discourse and serves us the nectar of wisdom.

Sannyāsa and tyāga – the threefold classification of tyāga (abandonment) – jñāna (knowledge), karma (action), kartā (doer, agent), buddhi (understanding), dhṛti (fortitude) and sukha (happiness) – the fourfold classification of humanity into brāhmaṇa, kṣatriya, vaiśya, śūdra – Self-perfection – final advice - the keynote of the entire *Gītā*.]

Arjuna: "Kṛṣṇa, tell me the essential features of sannyāsa (renunciatioin) and tyāga (abandonment) so that I can understand them".

Lord Kṛṣṇa: "Sannyāsa is the renunciation of ego and its desire prompted activities while tyāga is the abandonment of all anxieties to enjoy the fruits of action.

There are two schools of thought on sannyāsa. One school declares that all actions – religious and worldly irrespective of their quality, without any exception, should be avoided, as they would bring in more and more vāsanās, both good and bad. The second school is of the opinion that all good activities such as religious rituals, charity and austerity should be practised to advantage and only all other activities should be abandoned.

I shall explain 'tyāga' more clearly. Religious rituals, selfless service, charity and asceticism should not be abandoned, in my opinion. They really purify the mind. But remember that, even these should be performed with a detached mind.

Tyāga, abandonment is practised by people belonging to all types and there are three kinds of them: the sāttvika, the rājasika and the tāmasika.

That is sāttvika tyāga wherein one performs his duties promptly and well, with no attachment either to the action itself or to its result.[1] He acts in the right knowledge that the duties enjoined on him be discharged, not because he gets or wants to get anything from it for himself.

A true tyāgī is one, who performs his duties, whether they are agreeable or disagreeable. He does not look at one action as dignified and at another as undignified. He derives the same satisfaction from the performance of all kinds of work.

As long as an individual has got a physical body, throbbing with life he must work. Even existence is not possible without work.[2] But he should work

---

[1] कर्मण्येवाधिकारस्ते मा फलेषु कदाचन।
मा कर्मफलहेतुर्भूर्मा ते सङ्गोऽस्त्वकर्मणि ॥ २·४७ ॥
*karmaṇyevādhikāraste mā phaleṣu kadācana,*
*mā karmaphalaheturbhūrmā te saṅgo'stvakarmaṇi.* (2.47)

2.47. To action alone you have a right; never ever to the fruits thereof. Let not the fruits of action be your motive; never become attached to inaction.

[2] नियतं कुरु कर्म त्वं कर्म ज्यायो ह्यकर्मणः।
शरीरयात्रापि च ते न प्रसिद्ध्येदकर्मणः ॥ ३-८ ॥
*niyataṁ kuru karma tvaṁ karma jyayo hyakarmaṇaḥ,*
*śarīrayātrāpi ca te na prasiddhyedakarmaṇaḥ.* (3.8)

3.8. Perform the duties given to you; (For) to work, it is certain, is better than inaction. Even the survival of your body is not possible without work.

without worrying over the fruits that might spring from it. Such a one is a true tyāgī – a true man of abandonment. The threefold nature of the fruit of action can only be agreeable or disagreeable or mixed. All desire prompted activities must always produce one of these three results. An individual doing such actions, therefore, is always bound by the resultant vāsanās. The consequence is rebirth in order to experience the play of these new found vāsanās.

Those who abandon such actions altogether do not gather any vāsanās and so, they are not bound by ties to the world again.

There are five factors in the accomplishment of any action and they together comprise the 24 tattvas already enumerated (chapter 13.5).

They are: 1. Physical body; 2. The doer, the falsely conceived jīvātmā; 3. The five sense organs of perception; 4. The five organs of action; 5. The five great elements considered as the presiding deities of the five organs of perception.

All these five factors are always present in all actions – right or wrong – performed by the body, by the mind or by speech. In other words, matter (prakṛti) is the sole cause for all actions. The pure Self (Paramātman), not chained by any sense of possession of the body, the mind and the intellect has nothing to do with the action. He is only a witness. Therefore, that man, who considers his pure Self as the 'doer', is more to be pitied than to be condemned for his ignorance of the Truth.

The wise man, identifying himself with his Self acts in the full knowledge that it is matter envelopments that are active and not He, the Self. So, even when he kills, He the Self, does not commit a sin.

So, Arjuna, understand this Truth. You may take part in the battle. If you have detached yourself from your matter envelopments which alone are killing and have identified yourself with the pure Self within, you do not commit any sin. Your hands, metaphorically speaking, will not be stained by their blood. You should not have even a ray of doubt on this point.

The impulse, the urge to do (karma-kāṇḍa) is the sum total of these data. They are the 'knower' (parijñātā, the experiencer) who contributes the desire; the 'known' (jñeyam, the experienced) supplying the temptation to do it, and the 'knowledge' (jñānam, the experience) lending happy memories of it.

This urge is gratified with the help of the assembly (karma-saṁgrahaḥ), constituted of 1. The 'doer' (kartā), 2. The 'action' (karma) and 3. The 'equipments'.[1] There must be a classification of knowldege (jñānam) based on the three temperaments (guṇas). Knowledge can be brought under three types according to the temperaments that dominate in an individual. Thus, sāttvika jñānam is the best and the purest. The advaita philosophy, which teaches that the One is recognised as apparently manifest as many in the many living and non-living beings, is sāttvika. The philosophy of life that does not recognise the oneness from one another is rājasika jñānam – be it in religion or politics, in sociology or science.

The purely earthy mortals, sunk in wordly pleasures, consider themselves as divine and deny the existence of any higher power that guides all. Their absence of the right knowledge is tāmasika jñāna.

> [The 'doer' is ordered by his temperaments. Naturally there must be three kinds of actions

---

[1] The organs of perception and action, mind and intellect.

based on the three guṇas in the persons forming those actions.]

Sāttvika karma is that wherein the doer experiences a sense of joy and fulfilment, because it is not prompted by any sign of love or shade of malice. There is no attachment to it nor to its results. It is ever an inspired action.

Rājasika karma is that which is done to gratify a desire and the doer is quite conscious of his power in himself and his share which brought about the accomplishment of it.

Tāmasika actions are constituted of careless and irresponsible exertions which in the end, bring but sorrow and disaster upon himself and others.

[The threefold 'doer' (kartā) is here considered on the basis of the three types of men. Each doer has his own essential efficiencies.]

A sāttvika 'doer' is one who acts joyfully, with fortitude in the face of failures, and without egoism. He will not be loaded with expectations of reward while he works in his field of endeavour. He is unconcerned with its success and failure but discovers a satisfying delight in the very performance of the action with a spirit of loving dedication. It is ever to him a round of inspired activities. To him work means worship.

A rājasika 'doer' is one who acts with the motive of profit to himself. Elated in successes and dejected in failures, he is not reluctant to harm others to secure his interest. To him work means labour.

A tāmasika 'doer' is one, who calculates and plans for gaining for himself the maximum benefit out of a minimum effort. He postpones the discharge of his duties, at least as long as he can, and if possible, he avoids them altogether. He is ready to stoop down to any means to satisfy his brutal instincts. Arrogant and obstinate, cunning and complaining, he is an inimitable wretch.

> [The threefold classification of 'buddhi' (right understanding). The understanding of the three guṇa-types will be different from each other and they can be classified under three heads.]

Sāttvika buddhi is that capacity of the intellect to discriminate between constructive work and destructive work, between duties and forbidden actions, between fearlessness to accomplish what is right and fear to do what is wrong, between what will tie one to worldly existence and what will liberate one. Such an understanding is the right guide to lead us along the right path.

Rājasika buddhi is the capacity of the intellect to misconstrue the right and the wrong; what ought to be done and what ought not to be done.

Tāmasika buddhi is that obstinacy of the intellect to see the right as the wrong, to see duty as forbidden act, and to consider the forbidden act as the duty not to be avoided. In short, such an understanding will dictate only mistakes, and will arrive at only erroneous judgements.

[Threefold division of 'dhṛti' (fortitude): The capacity to discover in ourselves a new flood of inspired enthusiasm even when tired and exhausted is called fortitude.]

Sāttvika dhṛti is that firm fortitude to bounce up again, in spite of failures, to meet fresh challenges with fresh vigour, and the determination to reach the goal, not in the least deviating from the path pursued. This comes only from a complete mastery of the mind and all the sense organs. It also needs a clear and full vision of the goal by the intellect of this man of fortitude.

Rājasika dhṛti is the consistency of purpose in the pursuit of religious practices (dharma), acquisition of wealth (artha) and worldly pleasures (kāma) to gain happiness for himself.

Tāmasika dhṛti is the consistency that is seen in the stupid man who clings to fancies, stupidities, fear, grief, dejection and pride.

> [Sukha (happiness) can also have a similar threefold division as the happiness of the three types of men will vary in their qualities of intensity.]

Sāttvika sukha (happiness) is the abiding happiness, combined with a sense of security and fulfilment. This arises from self-purification by continuous self-discipline. To attain this happiness, one has to strive hard. So it is better and disagreeable like poison at first, but sweet and refreshing like nectar in the end. Many a passion prompted urges will have to be curbed and totally discarded. This is indeed painful. But in the end this brings the glaring happiness of a man of health and success.

Rājasika sukha is the fleeting joy, that is produced when the sense organs experience a thrill by coming in contact with their respective objects. It is intoxicating and exhilarating like wine at first, but soon it will bring weariness and a feeling of frustration. The happiness of indulgence is fleeting and it brings a revolting sense of exhaustion and ineffectiveness into the personality.

Tāmasika sukha is the dull joy one gets from sleep, indolence and from an existence in the flesh.

I have given you an exhaustive analysis of the three guṇas as seen manifest in the various fields of man's existence. The mortals and even the gods are conditioned by the guṇas in greater or a lesser degree. It is the proportion of these guṇas in a greater or a lesser degree that determines the personality, the behaviour and conduct of an individual.

[The classification of humanity into four psychological types – brāhmaṇas, kṣatriyas, vaiśyas and śūdras.

This may correspond roughly, in the modern days, to the learned and creative thinkers; the politicians and active leaders; the business men or the commercial men, the employer class; and the masses, the labourers who constitute the employee class.]

In connection with rebirth, I told you that each individual comes back to the world with a bundle of vāsanās, gathered from actions prompted by sattva, rajas and tamas. His birth in a particular family, in the given surroundings, is determined by his own past actions in his preceding births.[1]

Broadly, we may classify these personalities, according to their quality by their birth and by training, as the brāhmaṇas, kṣatriyas, vaiśyas and

---

1 अथवा योगिनामेव कुले भवति धीमताम्।
एतद्धि दुर्लभतरं लोके जन्म यदीदृशम्॥ ६·४२॥
*athavā yogināmeva kule bhavati dhīmatām,*
*etaddhi durlabhataraṁ loke janma yadīdṛśam.* (6.42)

6.42. Or, he is even born in the family of the wise yogīs; verily, a birth like this is very difficult to obtain in this world.

śūdras. The duties allotted to them are based upon their nature and fitness of each type to do the particular kind of work prescribed for them.

Tranquillity, self-control, asceticism, purity, patience and uprightness are to be practised by a brāhmaṇa in his daily life, in his relationship with other. He should study the scriptures and live up to the lessons learnt therein, with unquestionable faith and moral and spiritual heroism.

Martial valour, courage, fortitude, efficiency, generosity, leadership, and moreover, not running away from battle are the duties fixed for a kṣatriya by his station in life.

Therefore Arjuna, how can you, a royal prince (kṣatriya) justify your desire to run away from the battlefield? It is your moral duty to fight.[1] Do you not understand that a kṣatriya is predominantly a

---

[1] यदृच्छया चोपपन्नं स्वर्गद्वारमपावृतम्।
सुखिनः क्षत्रियाः पार्थ लभन्ते युद्धमीदृशम्॥ २·३२॥
*yadṛcchayā copapannaṁ svargadvāramapāvṛtam,*
*sukhinaḥ kṣatriyāḥ pārtha labhante yuddhamīdṛśam.* (2.32)

2.32. Happy indeed are the kṣatriyas, O Pārtha, who are called to fight in such a battle, that comes of itself, as an open door to heaven.

rājasika man, and hence, cannot, as you fancy, retire from war and sit successfully in contemplation, or wander on the face of the earth as a sage, living on alms. It is not in your nature and you will definitely fail if you attempt to live like a recluse.

Agriculture, cattle rearing and trade are enjoined on vaiśyas: and service in a spirit of dedication is the duty of the śūdras.

Loyal in the discharge of one's moral duties, one brings happiness, the ultimate goal of human endeavour – not only to himself but to others also. No one can find happiness in the pursuit of another's duties.[1]

Everyone should look upon the conscientious discharge of one's duty as an act of worship. Work should be an expression of your gratitude to God

---

[1] श्रेयान्स्वधर्मो विगुणः परधर्मात्स्वनुष्ठितात् ।
स्वधर्मे निधनं श्रेयः परधर्मो भयावहः ॥ ३·३५ ॥
*śreyānsvadharmo viguṇaḥ paradharmatsvanuṣṭhitāt,*
*svadharme nidhanaṁ śreyaḥ paradharmo bhayāvahaḥ.* (3.35)

3.35 (I count) Better is one's own duty though devoid of merit than the duty of another well discharged. Better is death in one's own duty; the duty of another is fraught with fear (is productive of positive dangers).

because it is He that lends His dynamism to your body to work. If one has this idea constantly in one's mind, no work would turn disagreeable and undignified.

God has a definite plan and a great purpose in placing an individual in a certain station in life. It is his duty to obey the Lord implicitly to discharge his duty faithfully and efficiently. He, the Lord, has chosen the duty for each, best suited to the individual's nature, and He knows that he can perform it much better than others.

No work be extolled or condemned. The faithful discharge of one's own duty is far better in every way, than even the very best performance of another's duty. No one incurs sins by the strict performance of one's own work which is in line with one's own vāsanās.

All activities without exception are enveloped by evil, as fire is by smoke, due to the three unavoidable guṇas. They always produce vāsanās. So, the best thing is: 1. To strictly perform the duty allotted to one according to one's station in life, and not to produce more vāsanās; 2. To get less entangled in worldly sufferings; and 3. To discharge one's duty by subduing one's own ego, and with the sense of agency in all activities. He, who is thus very active in the world but really inactive in spirit is a man growing to reach perfection. He becomes really fit to approach the God-state.

Factors essential to realise God, to enter into the God-consciousness are: a pure refined intellect; a firm mastery over the senses; fortitude; the sense organs rendered disinterested to the outside world of objects; a pure, clean mind which is not entertaining attachment and hatred; some love for solitude, moderation in food; silence; physical and mental discipline; conquest of egoism, brutal strength, arrogance, desire, anger, and avarice; freedom from the sense of possession and a constant attitude of cheerfulness.

These are the prerequisites essential for the success of a man of meditations. Such a wise man is released fully from grief and ambition, and is found ever to be calm and ever cheerful. His cup of happiness is always full. He is filled with love for Me. His love enables him to gain a full knowledge of Myself. He himself becomes divine.

Always taking refuge in Me and discharging your duties in the world, you enjoy the greatest enduring happiness. So always fix your mind on Me. Dedicate all your actions to Me in the firm faith that I am the ultimate Goal of human existence. Thus, you overcome all obstacles and attain salvation by My grace.

On the contrary, if you refuse in your pride and vanity to listen to this advice and to choose the right path – you will be embracing a sad ruin.

Now, coming to your particular case, Arjuna, you said that you would prefer the life of a beggar living upon alms to that of a prince. Do you still think so? In spite of My advice to the contrary, supported by the logical reasons, do you still believe that you should not fight? Then I tell you, it is only a superficial verbal assertion. Because in you, the kṣatriya is the inherent active nature (rajoguṇa) and it will assert itself and you will surely fight.

The Lord dwells in the heart of all beings, revolving them upon a machine as it were, made by His māya-power. Therefore, an individual is helpless to choose. 'My māyā', the vāsanās, in each one of us, shall decide what each should do and what each should not do. I repeat, dear Arjuna, you shall obtain supreme peace and happiness by your total surrender and dedicated service of the Lord in the form of the world.

I have already explained to you by now in this *Gītā*, the secret of the highest wisdom. I advise you to ponder over it, understand it well, and act accordingly.

Besides, you are very dear to Me and I shall advise you what is best for you. This is the essence of My teachings so far:

1. Fix your mind upon Me.
2. Have firm faith in Me.
3. Dedicate all your actions unto Me.
4. Totally surrender to Me.

Undoubtedly, you will reach Me. Do not forget – I am the only refuge. Come to Me in total self-surrender. I shall release you from all sins. Do not grieve.[1]

[1] सर्वधर्मान्परित्यज्य मामेकं शरणं व्रज ।
अहं त्वा सर्वपापेभ्यो मोक्षयिष्यामि मा शुचः ॥ १८.६६ ॥
*sarvadharmānparityajya māmekaṁ śaraṇaṁ vraja,*
*ahaṁ tvā sarvapāpebhyo mokṣayiṣyāmi mā śucaḥ.* (18.66)

18.66. Abandoning all dharmas, (of the body, mind and intellect) take refuge in Me alone; I will liberate thee from all sins; grieve not.

[The study of the *Gītā* – how can we become fully fit to gain this knowledge easily? The glory of the studying and teaching of *Bhagavad-gītā*.]

This profound teaching should not be imparted to those who do not have mental discipline, a firm faith in Me, a consummate love for selfless service and above all, the inspiring urge to reach Me.

The teacher who imparts the *Gītā* knowledge to earnest spiritual students will also be released from the agonies of worldly existence of desires and passions. He does the greatest service to Me by spreading spiritual knowledge and hence, he is dearest to Me.

I consider the study of the *Gītā* as a great sacrifice, jñāna-yajña. Because the student offers his ignorance to be burnt up in the fire of knowledge so kindled in him through a sincere study of the *Gītā*-theme and practice of its techniques.

Even those who listen to the *Gītā* with faith in Me reach the land of the meritorious, the world of peace and joy.

May I know, Arjuna, whether you have been listening to Me attentively? Could I dispel the darkness of your delusion?"

Arjuna: "Yes, Kṛṣṇa, I have clearly underestood Your lessons. My delusion is completely gone by Your grace. I am fully enligthtened as to what my duty is. I shall implicitly obey you. I promise".

---

यज्ञदानतपःकर्म न त्याज्यं कार्यमेव तत्।
यज्ञो दानं तपश्चैव पावनानि मनीषिणाम्॥ १८·५॥

*yajñadānatapaḥkarma na tyājyaṁ kāryameva tat,*
*yajño dānaṁ tapaścaiva pāvanāni manīṣiṇām.* (18.5)

18.5 Acts of sacrifice, charity and austerity should not be abandoned, but should be performed; worship, charity and also austerity are the purifiers of the wise.

न हि देहभृता शक्यं त्यक्तुं कर्माण्यशेषतः।
यस्तु कर्मफलत्यागी स त्यागीत्यभिधीयते॥ १८·११॥

*na hi dehabhṛtā śakyaṁ tyaktuṁ karmāṇyaśeṣataḥ,*
*yastu karmaphalatyāgī sa tyāgītyabhidhīyate.* (18.11)

18.11 Verily, it is not possible for an embodied being to abandon actions entirely, but he who relinquishes 'the fruit of actions' is verily called relinquisher (tyāgī).

नियतं सङ्गरहितमरागद्वेषतः कृतम् ।
अफलप्रेप्सुना कर्म यत्तत्सात्त्विकमुच्यते ॥१८·२३॥

*niyataṁ saṅgarahitamarāgadveṣataḥ kṛtam,*
*aphalaprepsunā karma yattatsāttvikamucyate.* (18.23)

18.23 An action which is ordained, which is free from attachment, which is done without love or hatred, by one not desirous of the fruit, that action is declared to be sāttvika (pure).

ब्राह्मणक्षत्रियविशां शूद्राणां च परन्तप ।
कर्माणि प्रविभक्तानि स्वभावप्रभवैर्गुणैः ॥ १८·४१ ॥

*brāhmaṇakṣatriyaviśāṁ śūdrāṇāṁ ca parantapa,*
*karmāṇi pravibhaktāni svabhāvaprabhavairguṇaiḥ.* (18.41)

18.41 Of scholars (brāhmaṇas), leaders (kṣatriyas) and traders (vaiśyas), as also of workers (śūdras), O Parantapa, the duties are distributed according to the qualities born of thier own nature.

शमो दमस्तपः शौचं क्षान्तिरार्जवमेव च ।
ज्ञानं विज्ञानमास्तिक्यं ब्रह्मकर्म स्वभावजम् ॥ १८·४२ ॥

*śamo damastapaḥ śaucaṁ kṣāntirārjavameva ca,*
*jñānaṁ vijñānamāstikyaṁ brahmakarma svabhāvajam.* (18.42)

18.42 Serenity, self-restraint, austerity, purity, forgiveness and also uprightness, knowledge, realisation, belief in God are the duties of the brāhmaṇas, born of (their own) nature.

शौर्यं तेजो धृतिर्दाक्ष्यं युद्धे चाप्यपलायनम् ।
दानमीश्वरभावश्च क्षात्रं कर्म स्वभावजम् ॥ १८·४३ ॥

*śauryaṁ tejo dhṛtirdākṣyaṁ yuddhe cāpyapalāyanam,*
*dānamīśvarabhāvaśca kṣātraṁ karma svabhāvajam* . (18.43)

18.43 Prowess, splendour, firmness, dexterity, and also not fleeing from battle, generosity and lordliness, these are the duties of the kṣatriyas, born of (their own) nature.

कृषिगौरक्ष्यवाणिज्यं वैश्यकर्म स्वभावजम् ।
परिचर्यात्मकं कर्म शूद्रस्यापि स्वभावजम् ॥ १८·४४ ॥

*kṛṣigaurakṣyavāṇijyaṁ vaiśyakarma svabhāvajam,*
*paricaryātmakaṁ karma śūdrasyāpi svabhāvajam.* (18.44)

18.44 Agriculture, cattle-rearing and trade are the duties of the vaiśyas, born of (their own) nature; and service is the duty of śūdras, born of (their own) nature.

श्रेयान्स्वधर्मो विगुणः परधर्मात्स्वनुष्ठितात् ।
स्वभावनियतं कर्म कुर्वन्नाप्नोति किल्बिषम् ॥ १८·४७ ॥

*śreyānsvadharmo viguṇaḥ paradharmātsvanuṣṭhitāt,*
*svabhāvaniyataṁ karma kurvannāpnoti kilbiṣam.* (18.47)

18.47 Better one's own duty (though) destitute of merits, than the duty of another well performed. He who does the duty ordained by his own nature incurs no sin.

सहजं कर्म कौन्तेय सदोषमपि न त्यजेत् ।
सर्वारम्भा हि दोषेण धूमेनाग्निरिवावृताः ॥ १८·४८ ॥

*sahajaṁ karma kaunteya sadoṣamapi na tyajet,*
*sarvārambhā hi doṣeṇa dhūmenāgnirivāvṛtāḥ.* (18.48)

18.48 One should not abandon, O Kaunteya, the duty to which one is born, though faulty, for all undertakings are enveloped by evil, as fire by smoke.

मच्चित्तः सर्वदुर्गाणि मत्प्रसादात्तरिष्यसि ।
अथ चेत्त्वमहङ्कारान्न श्रोष्यसि विनङ्क्ष्यसि ॥ १८·५८ ॥

*maccittaḥ sarvadurgāṇi matprasādāttariṣyasi,*
*atha cettvamahaṅkārānna śroṣyasi vinaṅkṣyasi.* (18.58)

18.58 Fixing your mind on Me, you shall by My grace, overcome all obstacles, but if, from egoism, you will not hear Me, you shall perish.

ईश्वरः सर्वभूतानां हृद्देशेऽर्जुन तिष्ठति ।
भ्रामयन्सर्वभूतानि यन्त्रारूढानि मायया ॥ १८·६१ ॥

*īśvaraḥ sarvabhūtānāṁ hṛddeśe'rjuna tiṣṭhati,*
*bhrāmayansarvabhūtāni yantrārūḍhāni māyayā.* (18.61)

18.61 The Lord dwells in the hearts of all beings, O Arjuna, causing all beings, by His illusive power, to revolve, as if mounted on a machine.

तमेव शरणं गच्छ सर्वभावेन भारत ।
तत्प्रसादात्परां शान्तिं स्थानं प्राप्स्यसि शाश्वतम् ॥ १८·६२ ॥

*tameva śaraṇaṁ gaccha sarvabhāvena bhārata,*
*tatprasādātparāṁ śāntiṁ sthānaṁ prapsyasi śāśvatam.* (18.62)

18.62 Fly unto Him for refuge with all your being, O Bhārata; by His grace you shall obtain supreme peace (and) the eternal abode.

सर्वधर्मान्परित्यज्य मामेकं शरणं व्रज ।
अहं त्वा सर्वपापेभ्यो मोक्षयिष्यामि मा शुचः ॥ १८·६६ ॥

*sarvadharmānparityajya māmekaṁ śaraṇaṁ vraja,*
*ahaṁ tvā sarvapāpebhyo mokṣayiṣyāmi mā śucaḥ.* (18.66)

18.66 Abandoning all dharmas of the body, mind and intellect, take refuge in Me alone; I will liberate you from all sins; grieve not.

**यत्र योगेश्वरः कृष्णो यत्र पार्थो धनुर्धरः ।**
**तत्र श्रीर्विजयो भूतिर्ध्रुवा नीतिर्मतिर्मम ॥ १८ · ७८ ॥**

*yatra yogeśvaraḥ kṛṣṇo yatra pārtho dhanurdharaḥ,*
*tatra śrīrvijayo bhūtirdhruvā nītirmatirmama.* (18.78)

18.78 Wherever is Kṛṣṇa, the Lord of yoga, wherever is Pārtha, the archer, there is prosperity, victory, happines and firm (steady or sound) policy; such is My conviction.

---

## Questions on Chapter XVIII

1. What are the essential features of sannyāsa and tyāga? (2)
2. What are the two schools of thought on sannyāsa? (3)
3. Explain in your own words the means of tyāga? (5, 6)

4. What is sāttvika tyāga? (9-10)
5. Who is a true tyāgī? (8-9)
6. What are the causes for the rebirth? (12)
7. What are the five factors in the accomplishment of an action? (14)
8. What is the sole cause for all the actions? (15)
9. 'He is to be pitied'. – Who and why? (16)
10. 'You should not have even a ray of doubt on the point'. On what point? (17)
11. What do you mean by karma-saṁgrahaḥ? (18)
12. What are the four classifications of humanity and what are their duties? (41)
13. Who is really fit to approach the God-state? (45, 46, 49, 50)
14. What are the factors essential to realise God? (51-54)
15. How can you obtain supreme peace and happiness? (55-57)
16. Give in your own words the essence of Lord Kṛṣṇa's teachings so far. (66)

17. Explain the following with reference to the context.
    (a) If one has 'this' idea constantly in one's mind, no work would turn disagreeable and undignified. (47-48)
    (b) 'I am the only refuge'. (66)
    (c) 'And hence, he is the dearest to Me'. (68-69)
    (d) 'Thus you overcome all obstacles and attain salvation by My grace'. (58)
18. Write short notes on the following:
    (a) Knower; known; knowledge (16)
    (b) Three kinds of jñānam (20-22)
    (c) Three kinds of karma (23-25)
    (d) Three kinds of 'doer' (26-28)
    (e) Three kinds of buddhi(30-32)
    (f) Three kinds of dhṛti or fortitude (33-35)
    (g) Three kinds of sukha (37-39)

**Om Tat Sat**